HOLT CALIFORNIA

Life Science

Study Guide B
with Directed Reading Worksheets

HOLT, RINEHART AND WINSTON

A Harcourt Education Company

Orlando • **Austin** • New York • San Diego • London

TO THE STUDENT

Do you need to review the concepts in the text? If so, this booklet will help you. The *Study Guide* is an important tool to help you organize what you have learned from the chapter so that you can succeed in your studies. The booklet contains a Directed Reading worksheet and a Vocabulary and Section Summary worksheet for each section of the chapter.

Use these worksheets in the following ways:

• as a reading guide to identify and study the main concepts of each chapter before or after you read the text

• as a place to record and review the main concepts and definitions from the text

• as a reference to determine which topics you have learned well and which topics you may need to study further

ISBN-10: 0-03-099397-0
ISBN-13: 978-0-03099-397-8

13 14 15 1409 14 13 12
4500356886

Contents

Name _____ Class _____ Date _____

Skills Worksheet)

Directed Reading B

Section: Scientific Methods (pp. 12–19)
WHAT ARE SCIENTIFIC METHODS?

1. The first step in using scientific methods is asking questions. Name two steps that follow.

_____

_____

2. Why do scientists vary the order of the steps of scientific methods?

_____

_____

ASK A QUESTION

3. When you observe something out of the ordinary or difficult to explain, what might you do?

_____

_____

MAKE OBSERVATIONS

_____ **4.** Observations are useful only if they are
   a. important.
   b. accurate.
   c. complicated.
   d. understood.

5. What did students in Minnesota do with their data and observations after they examined the frogs?

_____

_____

6. What is an observation?

_____

_____

7. What are some tools that scientists use to make observations?

_____

_____

FORM A HYPOTHESIS

8. A possible explanation or answer to a question is a(n)

_____.

9. What is a hypothesis based on?

_____

10. A hypothesis must be able to be _____ in order to be useful.

11. What were three hypotheses that scientists formed about what caused deformation in frogs?

_____

_____

_____

12. A statement of cause and effect that can be used to set up a test for a

hypothesis is called a(n) _____.

13. In what format is a scientist's statement of cause and effect usually stated?

_____

TEST THE HYPOTHESIS

14. What is a controlled experiment?

_____

_____

15. What is a variable?

_____

_____

16. Designing an experiment requires _____.

17. What kind of guidelines must scientists use in designing and conducting an experiment?

_____

18. How should scientists care for animals, such as the frogs in experiments with UV light?

_____

_____

19. Why do scientists try to test many individuals?

_____

_____

20. What is one way that scientists can support their conclusions?

_____

_____

ANALYZE THE RESULTS

21. How might a scientist organize data in order to analyze them?

_____

22. What does analyzing the results help a scientist to do?

_____

_____

DRAW CONCLUSIONS

_____ **23.** What did the UV light experiment prove about frog deformities?
   a. that they can be caused by UV light
   b. that they cannot be caused by UV light
   c. that the deformities of frogs in Minnesota were definitely caused by UV light
   d. that no Minnesota frogs were harmed by UV light

24. Why is proving that a hypothesis is wrong just as helpful as supporting it?

_____

_____

_____

25. Finding an answer to a question often leads to _____.

COMMUNICATE RESULTS

26. What are two reasons that scientists share their results?

_____

_____

_____

Directed Reading B

Section: Tools and Measurement (pp. 20–25)

1. What do life scientists use tools for?

_____

_____

TECHNOLOGY IN SCIENCE

2. What is technology?

_____

_____

3. What are two ways that computers and calculators help scientists?

_____

_____

_____

4. What is another way in which scientists use computers?

_____

_____

_____

Match the correct description with the correct term. Write the letter in the space provided.

_____ 5. bounces electrons off the surface of a specimen to produce a three-dimensional image

_____ 6. passes electrons through a specimen to produce a flat image

_____ 7. uses light and lenses to magnify small objects so they can be seen

_____ 8. focuses a beam of electrons to magnify small objects

_____ 9. is used by scientists to make observations from a distance

a. compound light microscope

b. scanning electron microscope

c. binoculars

d. electron microscope

e. transmission electron microscope

MEASUREMENT

_____ **10.** Many standardized units of measurement were once based on
    a. the weather.
    b. mythology.
    c. parts of the body.
    d. ancient worldwide standards.

11. What are two advantages of using the International System of Units?

_____

_____

_____

12. What unit of measurement would a life scientist use to describe the length of an ant?

_____

13. A measure of the size of the surface of an object or region is its

_____.

14. The units for area are called _____ units.

15. What is the term used to describe the size of something in three-dimensional space?

_____

16. What SI units of measurement are used to describe the volume of liquids and solids?

_____

_____

_____

17. What does 1 mL of a liquid equal in cubic centimeters?

_____

18. How would you find the volume of a box-shaped object?

_____

19. How would you find the volume of an irregularly shaped object?

_____

_____

20. What tool is used in science to measure the volume of a liquid?

_____

21. A measure of the amount of matter of an object is its

_____.

22. Why is the mass of an object constant any place in the universe?

_____

23. What units of measurement are used to describe an object's amount of matter, or mass?

_____

24. What is weight?

_____

25. Why is the weight of an object on Earth different from its weight on the moon?

_____

26. What is temperature a measure of?

_____

Match the correct description with the correct term. Write the letter in the space provided.

_____ 27. an indication of the amount of energy within matter

_____ 28. a tool used to show temperature

_____ 29. official SI base units for describing temperature

_____ 30. units commonly used by scientists to describe temperature

a. kelvins

b. temperature

c. degrees Celsius

d. thermometer

Skills Worksheet

Directed Reading B

Section: Scientific Models and Knowledge (pp. 26–31)
TYPES OF SCIENTIFIC MODELS

_____ 1. What is a representation of an object or a system called?
  a. the real thing
  b. a structure
  c. a model
  d. a prediction

_____ 2. What is a limitation of models?
  a. They are never exactly like the real thing.
  b. They are too small to be used.
  c. They are only concepts.
  d. They are on computers.

_____ 3. What are three types of scientific models?
  a. physical, mathematical, and conceptual
  b. small, medium, and large
  c. atomic, molecular, and elemental
  d. animal, vegetable, and mineral

_____ 4. Which is an example of a physical model?
  a. an equation
  b. a microscope
  c. a toy rocket
  d. human bones

_____ 5. What may a mathematical model be made up of?
  a. plastic organs and bones
  b. paint and plaster
  c. concepts and computers
  d. numbers and equations

_____ 6. Which is an example of a mathematical model?
  a. a map
  b. a graph
  c. an action figure
  d. a theory

_____ 7. It is NOT true that computers
  a. make fewer mistakes than humans.
  b. are useful for creating mathematical models.
  c. always make correct models.
  d. can keep track of more variables than humans can.

_____ **8.** Which of the following is a conceptual model?
  a. a diagram of scientific methods
  b. a model dinosaur skeleton
  c. $6 \times 2 + 2 = 14$
  d. a plastic human heart

9. What is a conceptual model?

_____

_____

USING SCALE IN MODELS

_____ **10.** Which of the following models would NOT use scale?
  a. a model of a sailing ship
  b. an equation
  c. a road map
  d. a floor plan of a house

11. What does scale represent?

_____

_____

12. Why can scale models, maps, and diagrams accurately communicate scientific knowledge?

_____

_____

BENEFITS OF MODELS

_____ **13.** A model can be a kind of testable
  a. question.
  b. dinosaur.
  c. variable.
  d. hypothesis.

14. What can models be used to represent?

_____

_____

_____

BUILDING SCIENTIFIC KNOWLEDGE

_____ **15.** An explanation that ties together many related facts, observations, and tested hypotheses is called a scientific
  a. law.
  b. result.
  c. theory.
  d. scale.

_____ **16.** A summary of many experimental results and observations that rarely changes is called a scientific
  a. law.
  b. result.
  c. theory.
  d. scale.

17. A theory is a(n) _____ model.

18. What is the difference between scientific theory and scientific law?

_____

_____

_____

19. Why are there very few laws within life science?

_____

_____

20. What is one widely accepted theory in life science?

_____

_____

21. What idea does the discovery about *Apatosaurus's* neck illustrate?

_____

22. What are two general characteristics of a theory that would be accepted by most scientists?

_____

_____

_____

Skills Worksheet

Directed Reading B

Section: Safety in Science (pp. 32–37)
THE IMPORTANCE OF SAFETY RULES

1. What is safety?

_____

_____

2. In science class what is the most important safety rule?

_____

_____

3. What is the most important reason for obeying safety rules?

_____

4. Once an accident has happened, how can following safety rules help you?

_____

_____

ELEMENTS OF SAFETY

_____ **5.** Safety symbols alert you to
  a. first-aid instructions.
  b. more science activities.
  c. ways to please your teacher.
  d. potential dangers.

_____ **6.** Which of the following are on your chart of safety symbols?
  a. water safety, boating safety
  b. automotive safety, traffic safety
  c. football safety, skateboard safety
  d. electrical safety, chemical safety

_____ **7.** What should you do if you can't understand instructions in a lab procedure?
  a. Ask your teacher to explain the directions.
  b. Ask your friend for help.
  c. Do whatever you think is correct.
  d. Start the lab all over again.

_____ **8.** What should you do if you find a bookpack, your lunch, and your math book on your lab work area?

   a. Leave them there so they won't get lost.

   b. Use them in the activity.

   c. Clear them away so they won't be in the way.

   d. Find out who put them there.

_____ **9.** If you need to handle chemicals, animals, or insects, you should

   a. use your apron to hold them.

   b. wear protective gloves.

   c. get someone else to handle them for you.

   d. stop working on the activity.

_____ **10.** What should you do with glassware at the end of an activity?

   a. Ask your lab partner what to do with it.

   b. Take it home.

   c. Throw it in the garbage.

   d. Wash it, and check it for cracks and chips.

11. What are the rules for handling animals used in science activities?

_____

_____

_____

_____

_____

Match the correct example with the correct element of safety. Write the letter in the space provided.

_____ **12.** preparing data tables and gathering safety equipment

_____ **13.** reading all instructions before beginning a science lab

_____ **14.** recognizing what a picture of a hand means

_____ **15.** wiping your work area with a wet paper towel

_____ **16.** wearing goggles and an apron

a. recognizing safety symbols

b. reading and following directions

c. practicing neatness

d. using proper safety equipment

e. following proper cleanup procedures

Directed Reading B *continued*

PROPER ACCIDENT PROCEDURES

17. List in the correct order the four steps to do after an accident.

_____

_____

_____

_____

18. Why should you know where emergency equipment is kept?

_____

_____

_____

PROPER FIRST-AID PROCEDURES

19. What is first aid?

_____

_____

Match the correct injury with the correct first-aid procedure. Write the letter in the space provided.

_____ **20.** small cuts

_____ **21.** chemical in eye

_____ **22.** minor heat-related burn

_____ **23.** chemicals on skin

a. Rinse area with running water.

b. Hold affected area under cold, running water for at least 15 minutes.

c. Rinse with running water or in an eyewash.

d. Clean area, cover with a clean cloth or gauze pad, and apply pressure.

Skills Worksheet

Vocabulary and Section Summary B

Asking About Life

VOCABULARY

After you finish reading the section, try this puzzle! Match the correct definition with the correct term. Write the letter in the space provided.

_____ **1.** life science

_____ **2.** research

_____ **3.** observation

_____ **4.** experimentation

_____ **5.** environment

a. the search for answers to questions

b. an area and its characteristics

c. finding the answer to a specific question by conducting a carefully designed test or trial

d. the study of living things

e. taking note of something of interest

SECTION SUMMARY

Read the following section summary.

Science is a process of gathering knowledge about the natural world. Science includes making observations and asking questions. Life science is the study of living things.

To find answers to your questions, you can make observations, do experiments, or use print and electronic resources to do research.

Life science can help find cures for diseases, can research food sources, can monitor pollution, and can help living things survive.

Skills Worksheet)

Vocabulary and Section Summary B

Scientific Methods

VOCABULARY

After you finish reading the section, try this puzzle! In the space provided, write the term described. Then, find the words in the word search puzzle on the next page. Terms can be hidden in the puzzle vertically, horizontally, diagonally, or backward.

_____ **1.** a series of steps followed to solve problems

_____ **2.** a testable idea or explanation that leads to scientific investigation

_____ **3.** an experiment that tests only one factor at a time by comparing a control with an experimental group

_____ **4.** a factor that changes in an experiment in order to test a hypothesis

_____ **5.** something that actively contributes to the production of a result

SECTION SUMMARY

Read the following section summary.

• Scientific methods are the ways in which scientists follow steps to answer questions and solve problems.

• Any information gathered through the senses is an observation. Observations often lead to the formation of questions and hypotheses.

• A hypothesis is a possible explanation or answer to a question. A well-formed hypothesis may be tested by experiments.

• A controlled experiment tests only one factor at a time and consists of a control group and one or more experimental groups.

• After testing a hypothesis, scientists analyze the results and draw conclusions about whether the hypothesis is supported.

• Communicating results allows others to check the results, add to their knowledge, and design new experiments.

Vocabulary and Section Summary B *continued*

H	U	Y	T	H	W	P	L	O	B	B	D	M	S	L	I	Z	B	Z	T
H	X	T	I	U	U	A	E	P	P	X	N	X	C	L	B	B	N	N	A
C	S	C	S	G	G	N	H	A	S	V	I	U	D	Z	H	P	E	U	B
K	Q	D	O	X	A	P	R	N	Q	A	A	E	A	R	L	M	V	P	S
P	D	A	J	Z	Z	U	F	A	F	R	H	N	X	U	I	J	S	O	K
C	H	X	T	Y	A	E	G	B	K	I	N	F	E	R	O	V	I	A	R
A	I	Y	C	J	G	U	B	G	R	A	I	Z	E	C	T	E	I	J	Z
R	W	J	P	Z	P	G	I	X	R	B	X	P	H	L	F	B	O	Q	M
T	X	U	I	O	P	L	E	T	M	L	X	X	V	Y	R	Z	U	R	T
R	H	T	L	D	T	I	X	Q	N	E	C	N	H	P	P	D	G	D	
B	L	A	Y	I	X	H	E	J	D	V	S	Y	K	Q	P	O	M	E	G
Z	V	M	N	G	K	A	E	E	N	E	J	V	X	D	F	Y	T	P	C
J	W	D	F	U	D	Q	L	S	R	X	X	K	Y	E	Z	R	L	H	N
P	H	H	G	W	F	L	K	D	I	J	Z	R	J	T	O	S	O	P	E
J	Y	Z	L	N	O	B	T	T	S	D	G	V	T	D	Z	N	V	B	
R	S	V	J	R	P	D	E	V	C	I	V	F	C	F	D	O	M	A	C
F	P	G	T	T	R	U	B	H	P	R	Z	A	M	R	G	R	W	R	L
L	H	N	C	P	R	O	N	W	U	Y	F	P	G	M	H	R	N	I	O
F	O	X	G	Q	B	G	S	Y	K	U	Q	X	K	C	X	M	U	A	D
C	S	C	I	E	N	T	I	F	I	C	M	E	T	H	O	D	S	E	E

Skills Worksheet

Vocabulary and Section Summary B

Tools and Measurement
VOCABULARY

After you finish reading the section, try this puzzle! Using each of these clues, fill in the blanks provided below with the letters of the word or phrase described below.

1. the application of science for practical purposes

2. an instrument that magnifies small objects so that they can be seen easily by using two or more lenses

3. a microscope that focuses a beam of electrons to magnify objects

4. the measure of an object's surface

5. the measure of the size of a body or region in three-dimensional space

6. the measure of the amount of matter in an object

7. the measure of the gravitational force exerted on an object

8. the measure of how hot or cold something is

1. ___ ___ ___ ___ ___ ___ ___ ___ ___ ___

2. ___ ___ ___ ___ ___ ___   ___ ___ ___ ___ ___

  ___ ___ ___ ___ ___ ___ ___ ___ ___
     1

3. ___ ___ ___ ___ ___ ___ ___ ___

  ___ ___ ___ ___ ___ ___ ___ ___ ___ ___
                4

4. ___ ___ ___ ___
     3

5. ___ ___ ___ ___ ___ ___
     8   7

6. ___ ___ ___ ___

7. ___ ___ ___ ___ ___ ___
   2

8. ___ ___ ___ ___ ___ ___ ___ ___ ___ ___ ___
     9   6   5

Discover the phrase below by filling in the blanks with the letter above the matching numbers.

9. ____ ____ ____ ____ ____ ____ ____   ____ ____ !
   1   2   3   4   5   6   7   8   9

SECTION SUMMARY

Read the following section summary.

Life scientists use tools to collect, store, organize, analyze, and share data.

Scientists use technology such as calculators, computers, binoculars, and microscopes.

The International System of Units (SI) is a simple and reliable system of measurement that is used by most scientists.

Graduated cylinders measure the volume of liquids, rulers measure length, thermometers measure temperature, and balances measure mass.

You can calculate the area and volume of box-shaped solids by using measurements taken with a ruler.

Skills Worksheet

Vocabulary and Section Summary B

Scientific Models and Knowledge

VOCABULARY

After you finish reading the section, try this puzzle! Use the clues below to solve the following crossword puzzle.

ACROSS

2. A(n) _____ is a descriptive statement or equation that reliably predicts events under certain conditions.

4. A pattern, plan, representation, or description designed to show the structure or workings of an object, system, or concept is called a(n) _____.

6. A scientist is observing _____ when he or she is following a series of steps to solve problems.

DOWN

1. A(n) _____ is a system of ideas that explains many related observations and is supported by evidence.

2. The study of living things is called _____.

3. A(n) _____ is a testable idea or explanation that leads to scientific investigation.

5. _____ defines the relationship between the measurements on a model, map, or diagram and the actual measurement or distance.

SECTION SUMMARY

Read the following section summary.

A model is a representation of an object or system. Models often use familiar things to represent unfamiliar things. Three main types of models are physical, mathematical, and conceptual models.

Scale models, maps, or diagrams match the proportions of the objects they represent.

Scientific knowledge is built as scientists form and revise scientific hypotheses, models, theories, and laws.

Skills Worksheet

Vocabulary and Section Summary B

Safety in Science
VOCABULARY

After you finish reading the section, try this puzzle! Match the correct definition with the correct term. Write the letter in the space provided.

_____ **1.** first aid

_____ **2.** safety

_____ **3.** safety rules

_____ **4.** safety symbols

_____ **5.** safety equipment

_____ **6.** accident procedures

_____ **7.** first-aid procedures.

a. the state of being free of danger or injury

b. signs that alert you to potential dangers

c. a set of instructions to help reduce the damage that can happen if there is an accident

d. a set of instructions that you follow to prevent injury

e. emergency medical care for someone who has been hurt

f. a set of instructions to help someone who is hurt

g. supplies or gear that can protect you from injury

SECTION SUMMARY
Read the following section summary.

- Following safety rules helps prevent accidents and helps reduce injury.
- Five elements of safety are recognizing safety symbols, following directions, being neat, using proper safety equipment, and using proper cleanup procedures.
- Animals used in scientific research require special care.
- When an accident happens, you should assess the situation, secure the area, tell your teacher, and help your teacher with cleanup or first aid.
- First aid is emergency medical care. Some first-aid procedures can be done without training.

Skills Worksheet

Directed Reading B

Section: Characteristics of Living Things (pp. 52–55)
LIVING THINGS HAVE CELLS

1. All living things are composed of one or more _____.

2. The smallest functional and structural unit of all living organisms is

   called a(n) _____.

3. What is the role of the cell?

   _____

4. What is the purpose of the cell membrane?

   _____

   _____

5. Name three functions that different parts of a one-celled protist perform.

   _____

   _____

   _____

6. Name two kinds of cells that perform specialized functions in humans.

   _____

   _____

LIVING THINGS SENSE AND RESPOND TO CHANGE

7. What are all living things able to sense and respond to?

   _____

8. A change that affects the activity of an organism is called

   a(n) _____.

9. Name three examples of stimuli.

   _____

   _____

Directed Reading B *continued*

10. What must an organism be able to do to survive?

_____

11. Define *homeostasis*.

_____

_____

12. What is your body trying to do when you are either shivering or sweating?

_____

_____

_____

_____

13. How does a turtle control its body temperature?

_____

_____

LIVING THINGS REPRODUCE

14. The process by which two parents produce offspring that share

characteristics of both parents is called _____.

15. The process by which one parent produces offspring identical to the parent

is called _____.

16. Most animals and plants reproduce by _____.

17. Most single-celled organisms reproduce by _____.

LIVING THINGS HAVE DNA

_____ **18.** What do the cells of living things contain?
   a. hydrochloric acid
   b. phosphoric acid
   c. deoxyribonucleic acid
   d. sulfuric acid

_____ **19.** What does DNA do?
   a. carries instructions for the organism's traits
   b. breaks down food in cells
   c. acts as a stimulus in the environment
   d. acts as a preservative in foods

_____ **20.** How do parents pass on traits to their offspring?
    a. by maintaining homeostasis
    b. by responding to stimuli
    c. by passing on copies of their DNA
    d. by sweating or shivering

21. The passing of traits from parents to offspring is

    called _____.

LIVING THINGS USE ENERGY

_____ **22.** Which of the following is used to carry out chemical activities of life?
    a. DNA
    b. energy
    c. reproduction
    d. heredity

23. The sum of all chemical processes that occur in an organism is

    called _____.

LIVING THINGS GROW AND DEVELOP

_____ **24.** Which of the following statements about living things is NOT true?
    a. A single-celled organism shrinks and divides.
    b. Humans pass through different stages as they develop into adults.
    c. All living things grow during parts of their lives.
    d. Living things may develop and change.

Match the correct description with the correct term. Write the letter in the space provided.

_____ **25.** becomes larger and divides; makes other organisms   **a.** multicelled organism

    b. single-celled organism

_____ **26.** contains cells that get larger; becomes a bigger organism

Skills Worksheet)

Directed Reading B

Section: The Necessities of Life (pp. 56–61)

1. What are four basic needs of every organism?

_____

_____

_____

_____

WATER

_____ 2. Cells of most living things are made of approximately
   a. 10% water.
   b. 33% water.
   c. 50% water.
   d. 70% water.

_____ 3. Most of the chemical reactions involved in metabolism require
   a. air.
   b. oxygen.
   c. water.
   d. carbon dioxide.

4. About how long can humans survive without water?

_____

AIR

_____ 5. Air is mostly oxygen, nitrogen, and
   a. butane.
   b. carbon dioxide.
   c. kerosene.
   d. nitrogen dioxide.

_____ 6. During what chemical process do most living things use oxygen?
   a. releasing energy from food
   b. storing energy
   c. transporting waste
   d. breaking down cells

_____ 7. Green plants, algae, and some bacteria need carbon dioxide gas in
addition to
  a. carbohydrates.
  b. lipids.
  c. sugar.
  d. oxygen.

8. Green plants produce food and oxygen through the process

of _____.

9. Organisms that can live without air are _____.

A PLACE TO LIVE

10. What do all organisms need in the place where they live?

_____

_____

11. How does the limited amount of space on Earth affect organisms?

_____

_____

FOOD

12. What are two things that organisms get from food?

_____

_____

13. What do organisms use nutrients from food for?

_____

_____

_____

Directed Reading B *continued*

Organisms are grouped by how they get their food. The three groups are producers, consumers, and decomposers. In the space provided, write *P* if the word or
phrase describes a producer, *C* for consumer, and *D* for decomposer.

_____ **14.** eats other living organisms or organic matter

_____ **15.** mushroom

_____ **16.** frog

_____ **17.** uses energy from the sun or the chemicals in the environment
to make food

_____ **18.** plant

_____ **19.** gets energy by breaking down nutrients in dead organisms or
animal wastes

PUTTING IT ALL TOGETHER

20. What do all organisms need to do to food to use the nutrients in food?

_____

_____

21. Nutrients are made up of _____, which are substances
created when two or more atoms join together.

22. Molecules made of different kinds of atoms are called

_____.

23. Name the six elements that join together to form proteins, carbohydrates,
lipids, ATP, and nucleic acids.

_____

_____

_____

_____

_____

_____

PROTEINS

Match the correct description with the correct term. Write the letter in the space provided.

_____ **24.** molecules that join together to form new proteins

_____ **25.** proteins that start or speed up chemical reactions

_____ **26.** a protein found in red blood cells that binds oxygen and delivers it throughout the body

_____ **27.** a molecule involved in almost all life processes; needed to repair and regulate the body

a. enzymes
b. protein
c. amino acids
d. hemoglobin

CARBOHYDRATES

28. Molecules called _____ include sugars, starches, and fiber.

29. Carbohydrates provide and store _____ for cells.

30. Carbohydrates made of one sugar molecule or a few linked sugar molecules are called _____.

31. Name three examples of a simple carbohydrate.

_____

_____

_____

32. A carbohydrate made of hundreds of molecules linked together is called a(n) _____.

LIPIDS

_____ **33.** Which of the following statements about lipids is NOT true?
   a. Lipids mix with water.
   b. Lipids store energy.
   c. Lipids include fats and oils.
   d. Lipids form cell membranes.

34. The molecules that form much of the cell membrane are called _____.

35. Where can an organism get energy once it has used up most of its carbohydrates?

_____

_____

36. How do fats and oils differ?

_____

_____

37. How are lipids stored in plants and animals?

_____

_____

ATP

38. The main energy-carrying molecule in the cell is called

_____.

39. The energy in carbohydrates and lipids is transferred to

_____ to provide fuel for cellular activities.

NUCLEIC ACIDS

40. Molecules consisting of subunits called nucleotides are

called _____.

41. What is the role of nucleic acids?

_____

_____

42. When a cell needs to make a certain protein, it gets the directions from

the nucleotides in _____.

Skills Worksheet

Vocabulary and Section Summary B

Characteristics of Living Things
VOCABULARY

After you finish reading the section, try this puzzle! Use the clues provided below to solve the crossword puzzle.

ACROSS

1. the maintenance of a constant internal state in a changing environment

4. the smallest functional and structural unit of all living organisms

5. describes reproduction that does not involve the union of sex cells

DOWN

2. the sum of all chemical processes that occur in an organism

3. describes reproduction in which the sex cells from two parents unite to produce offspring

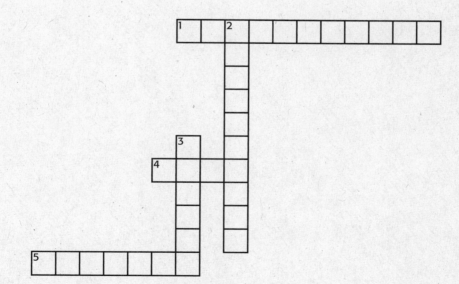

SECTION SUMMARY

Read the following section summary.

- Organisms are made up of one or more cells.
- Organisms detect and respond to stimuli.
- Organisms reproduce through sexual or asexual reproduction.
- Organisms have DNA.
- Organisms use energy to carry out their activities.
- Organisms grow and develop.

Skills Worksheet

Vocabulary and Section Summary B

The Necessities of Life
VOCABULARY

After you finish reading the section, try this puzzle! Use the clues below to fill in the blanks with the term being described. Then, find the vocabulary terms in the word search puzzle. Terms can be hidden in the puzzle vertically, horizontally, diagonally, or backward.

_____ 1. class of molecules that includes sugars

_____ 2. molecule made up of subunits called nucleotides

_____ 3. organism that eats other organisms for food

_____ 4. organism that breaks down the nutrients of dead organisms or wastes for food

_____ 5. molecules that form much of the cell membrane

_____ 6. organism that can make its own food

_____ 7. fat molecule that cannot mix with water and is used to store energy

_____ 8. large molecule made up of amino acids

_____ 9. molecule that is the main energy source for cell processes

Name _____ Class _____ Date _____

| Vocabulary and Section Summary B *continued*

K	D	G	S	Z	I	P	F	M	Y	Z	C	R	D	Q
P	T	R	J	R	U	H	J	S	C	A	R	E	N	S
E	I	F	Q	M	E	O	L	C	R	E	Q	M	Y	A
T	Y	P	M	B	X	S	F	B	C	G	J	U	P	M
P	W	N	R	M	F	P	O	U	U	G	Z	S	K	K
Z	I	Z	W	D	F	H	D	P	L	J	A	N	E	B
M	B	F	V	S	Y	O	X	H	M	I	Z	O	A	T
P	S	I	Z	D	R	L	W	F	C	O	P	C	D	H
P	I	I	R	P	J	I	V	Q	S	I	C	I	S	A
S	L	A	P	R	U	P	R	O	C	U	X	E	D	T
M	T	R	G	N	Z	I	F	T	T	I	K	R	D	P
E	O	J	J	A	C	D	J	Q	M	G	O	J	X	N
I	S	Z	Y	F	T	S	P	R	O	T	E	I	N	B
D	I	C	A	C	I	E	L	C	U	N	Q	W	D	G
D	E	O	X	N	B	B	H	F	Z	S	H	K	B	T

SECTION SUMMARY
Read the following section summary.

• The cells of living things need water to function.

• The cells of some living things need gases, such as oxygen, to release the energy contained in food.

• Living things must have a place to live.

• Cells store energy in carbohydrates, which are made up of sugars.

• Proteins are made up of amino acids. Some proteins are enzymes.

• Lipids store energy and make up cell membranes.

• Cells use molecules of ATP to fuel their activities.

• Nucleic acids, such as DNA, are made up of nucleotides.

Skills Worksheet

Directed Reading B

Section: The Electromagnetic Spectrum (pp. 76–81)

1. What kind of light can a bee see that you cannot see?

_____

2. In what way is visible light similar to ultraviolet light?

_____

_____

LIGHT: AN ELECTROMAGNETIC WAVE

_____ **3.** How is light different from other kinds of waves?
   a. Light does not need to travel through matter.
   b. Light does not differ in any way from other kinds of waves.
   c. Light must travel through matter.
   d. Light is not able to travel through matter.

4. What kind of wave is light?

_____

5. A wave that consists of changing electric and magnetic fields is called

a(n) _____.

A SPECTRUM OF WAVES

6. The entire range of EM waves is called the _____.

7. Which EM wave is only a small band within the broad electromagnetic spectrum?

_____

8. Name the seven kinds of EM waves.

_____

_____

_____

_____

_____

_____

9. List two examples of how EM waves are used in everyday life.

_____

_____

10. The distance from any point on a wave to an identical point on the next wave

is called a(n) _____.

INFRARED WAVES

_____ **11.** Which of the following statements about infrared waves is NOT true?
  a. Infrared waves from the sun make temperatures on Earth suitable
  for life.
  b. Infrared waves are only given off by the sun.
  c. Warmer objects give off more infrared waves than cooler objects do.
  d. All things give off infrared waves.

_____ **12.** What does the amount of infrared waves given off by an object
  depend on?
  a. the wave's speed and weight
  b. the wave's frequency and surface properties
  c. the object's weight and temperature
  d. the object's temperature and surface properties

VISIBLE LIGHT

13. The very narrow range of wavelengths in the electromagnetic spectrum that

humans can see is called _____.

14. What range of wavelengths can humans see?

_____

_____

15. What kind of energy is turned into chemical energy during photosynthesis?

_____

_____

16. The visible light of all wavelengths combined is called

_____

17. To the human eye, the longest wavelengths of visible light appear as the color

_____

18. To the human eye, the shortest wavelengths of visible light appear as

the color _____.

19. The range of colors of visible light is called the _____.

20. Name the seven colors of the visible spectrum.

_____

_____

_____

_____

_____

_____

ULTRAVIOLET LIGHT

21. In what way do ultraviolet waves differ from visible light waves?

_____

_____

22. Name four ways that the body can be harmed by overexposure to ultraviolet light.

_____

_____

_____

_____

23. Name two things that people can do to protect themselves against overexposure to ultraviolet light.

_____

_____

24. Describe two good effects of ultraviolet light.

_____

_____

Skills Worksheet

Directed Reading B

Section: Interactions of Light with Matter (pp. 82–89)

1. What does the special layer of cells in the back of a cat's eyes do?

_____

_____

REFLECTION

2. How does light travel when it travels through a material that doesn't change?

_____

_____

3. When light waves bounce off an object, _____ happens.

4. What does the law of reflection state?

_____

_____

_____

5. The arrival of a beam of light at a surface is called _____.

Match the correct description with the correct term. Write the letter in the space provided.

_____ **6.** line perpendicular to a mirror's surface

_____ **7.** angle between the reflected beam and the normal

_____ **8.** beam of light reflected off a mirror

_____ **9.** beam of light traveling toward a mirror

_____ **10.** angle between the incident beam and the normal

a. angle of incidence

b. angle of reflection

c. reflected beam

d. normal

e. incident beam

11. What is the difference between regular reflection and diffuse reflection?

_____

_____

_____

12. Why can a light source be seen in the dark?

_____

_____

_____

13. Objects that produce visible light are called _____.

14. An object that can be seen but is not a light source is

_____.

15. Why are you able to see an illuminated object?

_____

_____

ABSORPTION AND SCATTERING

_____ **16.** The transfer of light energy to particles of matter is called
   a. illumination.
   b. scattering.
   c. absorption.
   d. reflection.

_____ **17.** The interaction of light with matter that causes light to change its
   energy, direction of motion, or both is called
   a. reflection.
   b. scattering.
   c. absorption.
   d. incidence.

18. What causes the clear sky to look blue?

_____

_____

LIGHT AND MATTER

_____ **19.** The passing of light through matter is called
   a. transmission.
   b. scattering.
   c. absorption.
   d. incidence.

Name _____ Class _____ Date _____

Directed Reading B *continued*

20. When you look through a glass window, why can you see objects that are outside?

_____

_____

_____

21. When you look through a glass window, why can you see the glass and your reflection?

_____

_____

_____

_____

22. Why might a glass window feel warm when you touch it?

_____

_____

_____

23. Matter that allows visible light to be easily transmitted is

_____.

24. Matter that transmits light and scatters the light as it passes through the

matter is _____.

25. Matter that does not transmit any light is _____.

Match the correct description with the correct term. Write the letter in the space provided.

_____ **26.** glass

_____ **27.** wax paper

_____ **28.** metal

a. opaque

b. translucent

c. transparent

COLORS OF OBJECTS

29. What do humans see different wavelengths of light as?

_____

30. What is the color that an object appears to be determined by?

_____

_____

31. What happens when white light strikes a colored opaque object?

_____

_____

32. What colors of light are reflected by an opaque white object?

_____

_____

33. What colors of light are absorbed by an opaque black object?

_____

_____

34. Why is ordinary window glass colorless in white light?

_____

_____

35. What color of light do you see when you look through a colored transparent or translucent object?

_____

_____

36. What happens to the colors of light that are not reflected by or transmitted through a transparent or a translucent object?

_____

_____

PIGMENTS AND COLOR

_____ **37.** What is a pigment?
  a. a material that refracts colors of light
  b. a material that gives a substance its color
  c. a material that gives a substance its texture
  d. a material that transmits colors of light

38. Give two examples of pigments.

_____

_____

39. What happens when you mix pigments together? _____.

40. Mixing pigments involves a process called _____.

41. Name the three primary pigments that can be combined to make any other color.

_____

_____

_____

Skills Worksheet

Directed Reading B

Section: Refraction (pp. 90–97)
REFRACTION AND MEDIA

_____ 1. Refraction happens when
   a. a medium's density does not change.
   b. light follows the law of reflection.
   c. the wave changes light energy into chemical energy.
   d. the medium that it travels through changes.

2. A substance through which a wave can travel is called a(n)

_____.

3. The bending of a wave as the wave passes at an angle from one medium to

another is called _____.

4. Give an example of an optical illusion that can be caused by refraction.

_____

_____

_____

5. Light waves with _____ wavelengths bend more than

light waves with _____ wavelengths.

6. When white light separates into different colors during refraction and sunlight

is refracted by water drops, a(n) _____ forms.

LENSES AND REFRACTION OF LIGHT

_____ 7. How does a lens form an image?
   a. The lens reflects light.
   b. The lens bends light.
   c. The lens absorbs light.
   d. The lens transmits light.

Directed Reading B *continued*

Match the description with the correct term. Write the letter in the space provided.

_____ **8.** transparent object that forms an image by refracting light

a. focal length

b. lens

_____ **9.** point at which light beams cross after passing through a lens

c. focal point

_____ **10.** distance between the lens and focal point

Match the correct description with the correct term. Write the letter in the space below.

_____ **11.** is thicker in the middle than at the edges

a. convex lens

b. virtual image

_____ **12.** is formed when an object is less than 1 focal length from a convex lens

c. real image

_____ **13.** is formed when an object is more than 2 focal points from a convex lens

14. How do a real image and a virtual image of an object differ?

_____

_____

_____

15. How are a magnifying glass and the human eye similar?

_____

_____

16. Which two parts of the eye refract light?

_____

_____

17. Name two animals whose eyes process images differently than the human eye does.

_____

_____

18. What is the difference between a concave lens and a convex lens?

_____

_____

19. What happens to light rays when they travel through a concave lens?

_____

_____

20. What type of image can a concave lens form?

_____

_____

OPTICAL INSTRUMENTS AND REFRACTION

Match the correct description with the correct term. Write the letter in the space provided.

_____ **21.** opens and closes to control the amount of light that enters the camera

_____ **22.** focuses light on the film

_____ **23.** stores an image

a. film

b. lens

c. shutter

24. What does a digital camera use to record images?

_____

_____

25. What do the eyepiece lens and the objective lens in a refracting telescope do?

_____

_____

26. Name one way that a light microscope is similar to a refracting telescope.

_____

_____

27. Name one way that a light microscope differs from a refracting telescope.

_____

_____

Vocabulary and Section Summary B

The Electromagnetic Spectrum
VOCABULARY

After you finish reading the section, try this puzzle! Then, put the letters in the matching numbered squares on the next page to reveal a quote by Thomas Edison.

1. a type of electromagnetic wave that is used to kill bacteria on food

__ __ __ __ __ __ __ __ __ __ __ __ __ __ __
   1 18   13   2

2. a very narrow range of wavelengths in the electromagnetic spectrum that humans can see

__ __ __ __ __ __ __ __ __ __ __ __ __
 21   20 19

3. a type of electromagnetic wave that warms Earth

__ __ __ __ __ __ __ __ __ __ __ __
  12   3   5

4. the distance from any point on a wave to an identical point on the next wave

__ __ __ __ __ __ __ __ __ __
  16   22 8

5. the range of colors

__ __ __ __ __ __ __ __ __ __ __ __ __ __ __
  6   14

6. the entire range of electromagnetic waves, such as light, radio waves, microwaves, and X rays

__ __ __ __ __ __ __ __ __ __ __ __
              10   23

__ __ __ __ __ __ __
 7   4

7. the visible light of all wavelengths combined

__ __ __ __ __ __ __ __ __ __
  9

8. a wave that consists of changing electric and magnetic fields that vibrate at right angles to each other

— — — — — — — — — — — — — — — — — —
11   13   17   15

What Thomas Edison said:

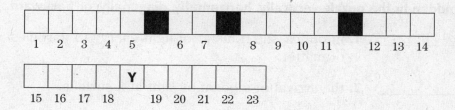

SECTION SUMMARY

Read the following section summary.

Light is an electromagnetic wave (EM wave). An EM wave can travel through matter or space.

The entire range of EM waves is called the *electromagnetic spectrum*.

Infrared waves from the sun warm Earth and everything on Earth.

Visible light is the narrow range of wavelengths in the electromagnetic spectrum that humans can see.

Humans see different wavelengths of visible light as different colors.

Ultraviolet light is both harmful and helpful to living things.

Skills Worksheet

Vocabulary and Section Summary B

Interactions of Light with Matter
VOCABULARY

After you finish reading the section, try this puzzle! Use the clues below to write the term described. Then, find those words in the puzzle on the following page. Terms can be hidden in the puzzle vertically, horizontally, diagonally, or backward.

_____ 1. in optics, the transfer of light energy to particles of matter

_____ 2. the arrival of a beam of light at a surface

_____ 3. the bouncing back of a ray of light, sound, or heat when the ray hits a surface that it does not go through

_____ 4. an interaction of light with matter that causes light to change its energy, direction of motion, or both

_____ 5. the passing of light or other form of energy through matter

R	N	C	Y	C	L	Z	S	R	F	L	E	Q	N	A
H	E	Q	X	N	Z	O	C	B	L	M	P	O	B	F
N	U	F	K	S	X	Y	A	C	K	Z	M	S	P	Z
H	A	Y	L	I	M	V	T	M	Z	S	O	Z	B	M
U	C	T	G	E	D	I	T	M	M	R	S	F	I	M
A	J	R	G	V	C	A	E	X	P	C	Q	V	D	U
T	C	M	S	P	D	T	R	T	Z	L	Q	Z	S	P
M	E	E	Q	O	X	R	I	H	H	N	I	C	X	B
B	A	W	E	Z	Q	O	N	O	D	H	Y	F	J	Y
H	K	E	M	C	N	Z	G	Y	N	Y	I	R	Y	D
T	R	A	N	S	M	I	S	S	I	O	N	O	Q	E
R	N	Z	P	Q	T	M	B	L	D	S	Y	D	V	E
G	K	V	C	N	R	B	A	K	D	R	L	O	W	K
Z	Y	Y	L	P	Q	U	G	E	C	A	B	N	W	L
E	C	N	E	D	I	C	N	I	S	E	M	U	N	A

SECTION SUMMARY

Read the following section summary.

Light travels in straight lines if the material that the light is traveling through does not change.

The law of reflection states that the angle of incidence is equal to the angle of reflection.

Things that are luminous can be seen because they emit light. Things that are illuminated can be seen because they reflect light.

Absorption is the transfer of light energy to particles of matter. Scattering is an interaction of light with matter that causes light to change direction.

Light can be reflected, transmitted, and absorbed by matter.

Colors of opaque objects are determined by the colors of light that they reflect.

Colors of translucent and transparent objects are determined by the colors of light they transmit and reflect.

Pigments give objects color. The primary pigments are magenta, cyan, and yellow.

Skills Worksheet

Vocabulary and Section Summary B

Refraction
VOCABULARY

After you finish reading the section, try this puzzle! Use the clues to unscramble each word below, and write it in the space provided.

1. a transparent object that is thicker in the middle than at the edges:
NXCVEO NSEL

___ ___ ___ ___ ___ ___   ___ ___ ___ ___

2. a substance through which a wave can travel: UIEDMM

___ ___ ___ ___ ___ ___

3. a transparent object that is thinner in the middle than at the edges:
VOCNAEC ESNL

___ ___ ___ ___ ___ ___ ___   ___ ___ ___ ___

4. the time between the arrival of P waves and the arrival of S waves:
NFACIREOTR

___ ___ ___ ___ ___ ___ ___ ___ ___ ___

5. a transparent object that refracts light waves such that they converge or diverge to create an image: SELN

___ ___ ___ ___

SECTION SUMMARY

Read the following section summary.

Light travels in straight lines if the medium through which the light travels does not change.

Refraction is the bending of a wave, such as light, as it passes at an angle from one medium to another.

Refraction of light can create optical illusions and can separate white light into different colors.

Lenses form images by refracting light.

Convex lenses produce both real images and virtual images.

A magnifying glass and the lens of the human eye are convex lenses.

Concave lenses produce only virtual images.

Cameras, telescopes, and microscopes are optical instruments that use lenses to form images.

Skills Worksheet

Directed Reading B

Section: The Characteristics of Cells (pp. 114–119)

1. The smallest functional and structural unit of all living organisms is

a(n) _____.

CELLS AND THE CELL THEORY

_____ **2.** What did Robert Hooke call the boxes cork seemed to be made of?
   a. bark
   b. rooms
   c. cells
   d. cartons

_____ **3.** What part of plant and fungus cells was easy for Hooke to see?
   a. cell membranes
   b. cell nuclei
   c. cell walls
   d. cell outlines

_____ **4.** In 1673, Anton van Leeuwenhoek saw single-celled organisms in
   a. distilled water.
   b. bath water.
   c. pond scum.
   d. salt water.

5. What kind of cells have cell walls?

_____

6. Today, the single-celled organisms Leeuwenhoek called *animacules*

are called _____.

7. What are the three parts of the cell theory?

_____

_____

_____

CELL SIZE

8. What is the yolk of a chicken egg?

_____

9. Where does a cell take in food and get rid of wastes?

_____

10. What limits the size of a cell?

_____

11. How is the surface area–to-volume ratio of a cell calculated?

_____

PARTS OF A CELL

Match the correct description with the correct term. Write the letter in the space provided.

_____ **12.** a protective layer that covers a cell's surface and acts as a barrier between the cell and its environment

_____ **13.** the fluid and its contents inside a cell

_____ **14.** a small body inside a cell's cytoplasm that performs a specific function in the cell

_____ **15.** the genetic material that carries information needed to make new cells and new organisms

_____ **16.** a membrane-bound organelle in a eukaryotic cell where the cell's DNA is stored

a. DNA

b. cell membrane

c. nucleus

d. organelle

e. cytoplasm

WO KINDS OF CELLS

17. What four parts do all cells have?

_____

_____

_____

_____

18. What are the two basic kinds of cells?

_____

_____

_____

19. Single-celled organisms without a nucleus are called

_____.

20. Describe the DNA of a prokaryote.

_____

_____

21. What are ribosomes?

_____

_____

_____

22. How do eukaryotes compare in size to prokaryotes?

_____

23. What does a cell of a eukaryote have to hold DNA that a cell of a prokaryote does not have?

_____

24. An organism made of cells that have a nucleus enclosed by a membrane

is a(n) _____.

Skills Worksheet

Directed Reading B

Section: Eukaryotic Cells (pp. 120–127)

CELL WALL

1. What rigid structure surrounds a plant cell membrane and provides support to the cell?

_____

2. What are the cell walls of plants and algae made of?

_____

_____

CELL MEMBRANE

_____ 3. What protective barrier separates a cell's contents from the cell's environment?
   a. the ribosomes
   b. the cytoskeleton
   c. the cell membrane
   d. the organelle

_____ 4. What two layers make it difficult for materials to pass through the cell membrane?
   a. phospholipid layers
   b. cytoskeleton layers
   c. hydrophilic layers
   d. hydrophobic layers

5. How do materials, such as nutrients and waste, pass through the cell membrane?

_____

_____

CYTOSKELETON

_____ 6. A web of proteins in the cytoplasm of plant and animal cells is known as the
   a. phospholipid.
   b. cytoskeleton.
   c. cell membrane.
   d. organelle.

_____ **7.** What gives animal cells their shape?
     a. the cell wall
     b. the cytoskeleton
     c. the cell membrane
     d. the exoskeleton

NUCLEUS

_____ **8.** In eukaryotic cells, genetic material called DNA is found in a membrane-bound organelle called the
     a. nucleus.
     b. nucleolus.
     c. nucleotide.
     d. cytoplasm.

_____ **9.** The function of proteins in a cell is to
     a. control chemical reactions.
     b. store genetic information.
     c. cover the nucleus.
     d. copy messages from DNA.

_____ **10.** A dark area of the nucleus where a cell begins to make its ribosomes is the
     a. mitochondrion.
     b. nucleolus.
     c. nucleotide.
     d. cytoplasm.

RIBOSOMES

11. Organelles that make proteins are called _____.

12. Proteins are made of _____.

13. Why do all cells have ribosomes?

_____

_____

_____

ENDOPLASMIC RETICULUM

14. A system of folded membranes found in a cell's cytoplasm, in which proteins,

lipids, and other materials are made, is the _____.

15. Endoplasmic reticulum (ER) that is covered with ribosomes is called

_____.

16. Endoplasmic reticulum (ER) that makes lipids and breaks down toxic

materials but lacks ribosomes is called _____.

MITOCHONDRIA

_____ **17.** In a eukaryotic cell, the organelle in which sugar is broken down to release energy is the
   a. ribosome.
   b. lysosome.
   c. endoplasmic reticulum.
   d. mitochondrion.

_____ **18.** Cells do work using energy released by mitochondria and stored in
   a. ATF.
   b. ALT.
   c. ATP.
   d. DNA.

CHLOROPLASTS

_____ **19.** The organelles in plant and algae cells where photosynthesis takes place are called
   a. ribosomes.
   b. chloroplasts.
   c. mitochondria.
   d. chlorophyll.

_____ **20.** The process by which cells, such as plant cells, use sunlight, carbon dioxide, and water to make sugar and oxygen is called
   a. respiration.
   b. oxidation.
   c. photosynthesis.
   d. parthenogenesis.

_____ **21.** Chloroplasts are green because they contain
   a. sugar.
   b. proteins.
   c. chlorophyll.
   d. DNA.

GOLGI COMPLEX

_____ **22.** What organelle packages and distributes proteins where they are needed?
   a. the endoplasmic reticulum
   b. the mitochondrion
   c. the central vacuole
   d. the Golgi complex

CELL COMPARTMENTS

23. The bubble that forms where a piece of the Golgi complex's membrane

pinches off is called a(n) _____.

24. What carries new protein from the ER to the Golgi complex and distributes material from the Golgi complex to other parts of the cell?

_____

LYSOSOMES

25. What is a lysosome?

_____

_____

26. In what kind of cells are lysosomes mainly found?

_____

27. What are three functions of lysosomes?

_____

_____

_____

VACUOLES

_____ **28.** Organelles in plant and animal cells that store digestive enzymes and aid in digestion within the cell are called
   a. vesicles.
   b. lysosomes.
   c. vacuoles.
   d. ribosomes.

_____ **29.** In plant cells, the organelle where water and other materials are stored and that helps support the cell is the
   a. endoplasmic reticulum.
   b. nucleolus.
   c. large central vesicle.
   d. large central vacuole.

Skills Worksheet

Directed Reading B

Section: The Organization of Living Things (pp. 128–133)

_____ 1. Anything that can carry out life processes independently is a(n)
   a. cell.
   b. organ system.
   c. tissue.
   d. organism.

2. What are the two types of organisms?

_____

_____

UNICELLULAR ORGANISMS

_____ 3. Organisms made of one cell are
   a. unicellular.
   b. multicellular.
   c. polycellular.
   d. megacellular.

4. What are two advantages to being unicellular over having many cells?

_____

_____

MULTICELLULAR ORGANISMS

_____ 5. Organisms made of many cells are
   a. unicellular.
   b. multicellular.
   c. polycellular.
   d. megacellular.

6. As a single cell develops into many cells, the cells become

_____, or fixed, into different types of cells.

7. What are two reasons the characteristic larger size of a multicellular organism is an advantage?

_____

_____

_____

8. Why does a multicellular organism usually have a longer life than a unicellular organism?

_____

_____

9. How does having specialized cells make an organism more efficient?

_____

_____

FROM CELLS TO ORGANISMS

_____ **10.** The special activity of an organ or part is its
   a. structure.
   b. differentiation.
   c. arrangement.
   d. function.

_____ **11.** The arrangement of parts in an organism, including the shape and material of which the part is made, is its
   a. structure.
   b. differentiation.
   c. arrangement.
   d. function.

12. Describe the structure and function of guard cells in some plants.

_____

_____

_____

_____

13. A group of similar cells that perform a common function is called

a(n) _____.

14. What are the four basic types of animal tissues?

_____

_____

_____

_____

15. Tissue that moves water and nutrients through a plant is called

_____.

16. Tissue that helps a plant retain water and protects the plant from damage

is called _____.

17. Plant tissue where photosynthesis takes place is called

_____.

18. A structure that is made up of two or more tissues working together to

perform a specific function is called a(n) _____.

19. What are three types of tissue that make up the heart?

_____

_____

_____

20. What are four types of tissue found in the stomach? What are their functions?

_____

_____

_____

_____

21. What organ in plants traps sunlight energy to make food?

_____

22. A group of organs that work together to perform a particular function is

called a(n) _____.

23. What organ system uses organs and tissues, such as the heart and blood vessels, to transport blood through the body?

_____

24. What are three organ systems found in plants?

_____

_____

_____

ORGANISMS

Match the correct description with the correct term. Write the letter in the space provided.

_____ **25.** first level of organization in multicellular organisms

_____ **26.** second level of organization in multicellular organisms; formed from cells

_____ **27.** third level of organization in multicellular organisms; formed from tissues

_____ **28.** fourth level of organization in multicellular organisms; formed from organs

_____ **29.** includes groups of organ systems

a. organ system
b. organism
c. tissue
d. organ
e. cell

UNICELLULAR ORGANIZATION

_____ **30.** Each cell carries out all life processes in order for that cell to survive in
   a. specialized organisms.
   b. multifunctioning organisms.
   c. unicellular organisms.
   d. multicellular organisms.

_____ **31.** One unicellular organism in which individual cells come together to form a large group is a
   a. eukaryote.
   b. plant.
   c. stoma.
   d. slime mold.

Vocabulary and Section Summary B

The Characteristics of Cells
VOCABULARY

After you finish reading the section, complete this puzzle. In the space provided, write the term described. Then find those words in the puzzle below. Terms can be hidden in the puzzle vertically, horizontally, diagonally, or backward.

_____ 1. one of the small bodies in a cell's cytoplasm that are specialized to perform a specific function

_____ 2. the repository for DNA in a eukaryotic cell

_____ 3. an organism made up of cells that have a membrane-bound nucleus

_____ 4. a protective layer that covers the cell's surface

_____ 5. a single-celled organism without a nucleus

_____ 6. the smallest functional and structural unit of all living things

O	J	Y	S	M	O	M	M	T	E	V	T	R	F	L
H	K	J	D	E	B	R	B	T	L	L	E	C	V	S
Q	P	G	K	M	Y	S	O	Y	V	N	R	J	U	E
A	N	S	J	B	H	Y	N	O	N	X	P	A	P	N
O	F	V	K	R	R	E	Q	R	M	O	D	S	U	A
V	M	M	L	A	S	Y	U	U	P	I	D	C	L	R
K	Q	C	K	N	B	O	G	K	B	B	L	D	B	B
Q	A	O	K	E	T	G	S	F	A	E	V	S	K	M
O	R	G	A	N	E	L	L	E	U	R	A	I	I	E
P	O	L	A	G	O	T	I	S	Z	M	Y	H	S	M
C	K	T	X	A	E	Z	U	U	W	F	K	O	H	L
V	U	M	H	E	K	A	S	V	T	O	W	K	T	L
X	A	N	F	S	C	A	U	F	E	H	Y	K	E	E
B	Q	F	X	L	D	I	J	Y	Z	S	H	B	D	C
U	Z	K	M	N	J	X	C	S	W	G	W	B	F	K

Vocabulary and Section Summary B *continued*

SECTION SUMMARY

Read the following section summary.

- The cell theory states that all organisms are made of cells, the cell is the basic unit of all living things, and all cells come from other cells.

- All cells have a cell membrane, cytoplasm, and DNA.

- Most cells are too small to be seen with the naked eye. The surface area–to-volume ratio of a cell limits the size of the cell.

- The two basic kinds of cells are prokaryotic cells and eukaryotic cells. Eukaryotic cells have a nucleus and membrane-bound organelles. Prokaryotic cells do not.

- Prokaryotes are single-celled.

- Eukaryotes can be single-celled or multicellular.

Skills Worksheet

Vocabulary and Section Summary B

Eukaryotic Cells
VOCABULARY

After you finish reading the section, use the clues below to complete the crossword puzzle.

ACROSS

5. a rigid structure surrounding the cell membrane

6. a web of proteins in the cytoplasm of some cells

7. a cell organelle composed of RNA and protein

8. a cell organelle that helps make and package materials to be transported out of the cell

DOWN

1. an organelle in plant and algae cells where photosynthesis occurs

2. a small cavity or sac that contains materials in a eukaryotic cell

3. a system of folded membranes in which proteins, lipids, and other materials are made

4. the main power source of a eukaryotic cell

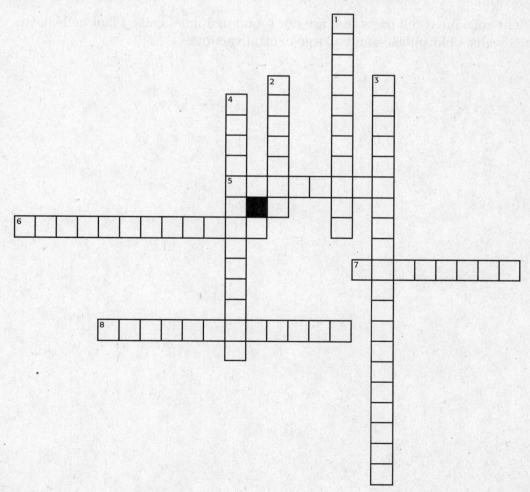

Vocabulary and Section Summary B *continued*

SECTION SUMMARY

Read the following section summary.

• Eukaryotic cells have organelles that perform functions that help cells remain alive.

• All cells have a cell membrane. Some cells have a cell wall. Some cells have a cytoskeleton.

• The nucleus of a eukaryotic cell contains the cell's genetic material, DNA.

• Ribosomes are the organelles that make proteins. Ribosomes are not covered by a membrane.

• The endoplasmic reticulum (ER) and the Golgi complex make and process proteins before the proteins are transported to other parts of the cell or out of the cell.

• Mitochondria and chloroplasts are organelles that provide chemical energy for the cell.

• Lysosomes are organelles responsible for digestion within a cell. In plant cells, the large central vacuole stores cell materials and sometimes acts like a large lysosome.

• Plant cells have cell parts that are not found in animal cells. Plant cells have cell walls, chloroplasts, and a large central vacuole.

Vocabulary and Section Summary B

The Organization of Living Things
VOCABULARY

After you finish reading the section, try this puzzle! In each of the following items, use the clue to unscramble the letters, and write the term in the corresponding blanks. Then, group the numbered letters together by number to find the hidden erm.

1. The activity that the cell performs: FTCNOINU

___ ___ ___ ___ ___ ___ ___ ___
                        1   5

2. A structure made up of two or more tissues working together to perform a specific function: NRGOA

___ ___ ___ ___ ___
   3

3. Anything that can perform life processes by itself: ONRIMAGS

___ ___ ___ ___ ___ ___ ___ ___
       2   4   10

4. The arrangement of parts in an organism: RSETUTCRU

___ ___ ___ ___ ___ ___ ___ ___ ___
   6   9

5. A group of cells that work together to perform a common function: SITUES

___ ___ ___ ___ ___ ___
   8   7

Hidden Term

A group of organs that work together to perform body functions:

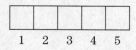

1	2	3	4	5

	Y			
6		7	8	9	10

SECTION SUMMARY

Read the following section summary.

- Unicellular organisms have only one cell.

- As a multicellular organism develops, its cells differentiate into specialized cells.

- Multicellular organisms are made up of one or many cells and can have a larger size and a longer life than unicellular organisms.

- The four levels of organization in multicellular organisms are cells, tissues, organs, and organ systems.

- A tissue is a group of cells working together. An organ is made up of two or more tissues working together. An organ system is made up of two or more organs working together.

Skills Worksheet

Directed Reading B

Section: Cell Energy (pp. 148–151)

1. Why do cells need energy?

_____

_____

2. Where do plant cells get their energy?

_____

3. Where do many animal cells get the energy they need?

_____

FROM SUN TO CELL

_____ 4. Where does almost all of the energy that fuels life come from?
   a. Earth
   b. gasoline
   c. plants
   d. the sun

5. Plants are able to change the sun's energy into food through a process

   called _____.

6. The molecules in plant cells that absorb light energy are called

   _____.

7. Plants get their green color from _____

8. Where are chloroplasts found?

_____

9. What is glucose?

_____

_____

10. Why is glucose important to a plant cell?

_____

_____

11. Photosynthesis produces _____ and

   _____.

Directed Reading B *continued*

GETTING ENERGY FROM FOOD

12. Cells use _____ to break down food using oxygen.

13. Many cells are able to get energy without using oxygen through a process

called _____.

14. Cellular respiration is a(n) _____ process that happens in
cells.

15. Describe what takes place during cellular respiration in complex organisms.

_____

_____

16. What does your body do with the energy released during cellular respiration?

_____

_____

17. Adenosine triphosphate, also called ATP, supplies _____
that fuels cell activities.

18. Cellular respiration in the cells of eukaryotes, such as plants and animals,

takes place in the _____ inside the cell.

19. During photosynthesis, plant cells use carbon dioxide to make glucose and
release oxygen. How is this different from cellular respiration?

_____

_____

_____

20. Why do you get a burning sensation in your muscles during strenuous exercise?

_____

_____

_____

Skills Worksheet

Directed Reading B

Section: The Cell Cycle (pp. 152–157)

1. Why is it important for your body to produce millions of new cells by the time you finish reading this sentence?

_____

_____

THE LIFE OF A CELL

_____ **2.** When does the cell cycle begin?
   a. when the cell is formed
   b. when the cell divides
   c. when the cell uses energy
   d. when the cell takes in oxygen

_____ **3.** When does the cell cycle end?
   a. when the cell is formed
   b. when the cell divides and makes new cells
   c. when the cell uses energy
   d. when the cell takes in oxygen

4. What must a cell do before it can divide to make a new cell?

_____

_____

5. What makes sure that each new cell receives all the DNA of the parent cell?

_____

_____

6. A cell without a nucleus is a(n) _____ cell.

7. A cell with a nucleus is a(n) _____ cell.

8. A chromosome is the main ring of DNA in a(n) _____ cell.

9. A chromosome is made up of DNA and protein in the nucleus of a(n)

_____ cell.

10. Are bacteria prokaryotic cells or eukaryotic cells?

_____

_____

11. Bacteria create new cells through a kind of cell division called

_____.

12. When binary fission is complete, the result is two cells that each contain

one copy of _____.

13. Eukaryotes have more _____ than do prokaryotes.

14. Humans have _____ chromosomes, while fruit flies have

only _____ and potatoes have _____

chromosomes.

15. Chromosomes that line up in pairs are made up of similar chromosomes

called _____.

16. In the beginning of the eukaryotic cell cycle, the cell grows and copies

its _____ and _____.

17. After a chromosome is duplicated, the two copies are

called _____.

18. Where are chromatids held together?

_____

_____

_____

19. What happens during the first stage of the cell cycle in a eukaryotic cell?

_____

_____

_____

_____

_____

20. What happens during the second stage of the cell cycle in a eukaryotic cell?

_____

_____

_____

_____

_____

21. The four phases of mitosis are

_____, _____,

_____, and _____.

22. What happens during the third stage of the cell cycle in a eukaryotic cell?

_____

_____

_____

_____

_____

23. Before mitosis begins, _____ are copied.

Use the diagram below to answer questions 24–29, which describe the phases of the cell cycle. Write the correct phase in the space provided for each question, using "Interphase," "Mitosis Phase 1," "Mitosis Phase 2," "Mitosis Phase 3," "Mitosis Phase 4," or "Cytokinesis."

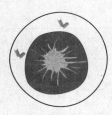
Interphase

Mitosis Phase 1

Mitosis Phase 2

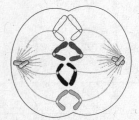
Mitosis Phase 3

Mitosis Phase 4

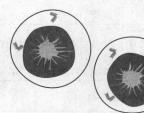
Cytokinesis

_____ **24.** The chromatids separate and move to opposite sides of the cell.

_____ **25.** The nuclear membrane is dissolved. Paired chromosomes align at the cell's equator.

_____ **26.** Before mitosis begins, chromosomes are copied.

_____ **27.** A nuclear membrane forms around each set of chromosomes, and the chromosomes decondense. Mitosis is complete.

_____ **28.** Mitosis begins. Chromosomes condense from long strands into rodlike structures.

_____ **29.** In cells that lack a cell wall, the cell pinches in two. In cells that have a cell wall, a cell plate forms and separates the two new cells.

30. How do animal cells without cell walls divide their cytoplasm during cytokinesis?

_____

_____

_____

_____

31. How do plant cells with cell walls divide their cytoplasm during cytokinesis?

_____

_____

_____

_____

_____

CONTROL OF THE CELL CYCLE

_____ **32.** After which stage in the cell cycle is each new cell an exact copy of the parent cell?
   a. interphase
   b. mitosis
   c. cytokinesis
   d. prophase

_____ **33.** Which of the following report cell conditions and control the cell cycle?
   a. feedback switches
   b. DNA
   c. homologous chromosomes
   d. centromeres

34. A tumor in which the cells begin dividing at an uncontrolled rate is called

_____.

Skills Worksheet

Vocabulary and Section Summary B

Cell Energy
VOCABULARY

After you finish reading the section, try this puzzle! Use the clues below to solve the crossword puzzle below.

ACROSS

1. word root meaning "green"
2. where chlorophyll is found
3. word root meaning "to form"
5. process using sunlight, CO_2, and H_2O to make food
7. plant molecules that absorb energy
8. word root meaning "light"

DOWN

1. process by which cells use O_2 to produce energy from food
4. breakdown of food without O_2
6. breathing

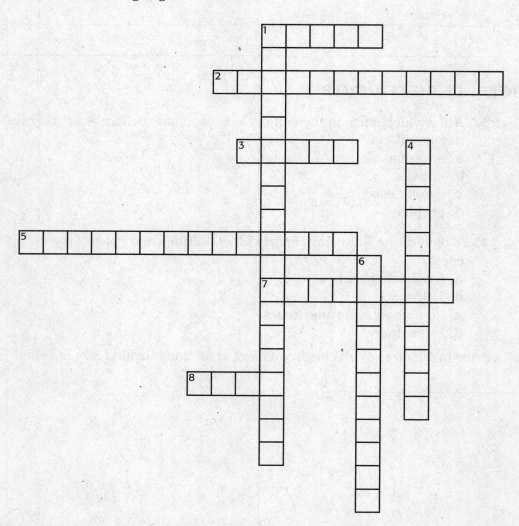

SECTION SUMMARY

Read the following section summary.

Most of the energy that fuels life comes from the sun.

The sun's energy is changed into food by the process of photosynthesis, which occurs in the chloroplasts of plant cells.

Cellular respiration breaks down glucose into water, carbon dioxide, and energy.

Cellular respiration takes place in the mitochondria of plant and animal cells.

Fermentation is a way that cells get energy from their food without using oxygen.

Name _____ Class _____ Date _____

Vocabulary and Section Summary B

The Cell Cycle
VOCABULARY

After you finish reading the section, try this puzzle! This game may be played individually or in teams. You are supplied with the answers to questions in three categories. Your challenge is to come up with the correct question for each answer. Each correct question has a point value corresponding to the number at the beginning of the row. Think carefully, as correct questions are used more than once! Keep a running total of your points as you play.

Points	To Make Two	Bringing Things to Life	I Can "C" You
25	• This is divided into four phrases	• The life cycle of a cell	• This process ends when a cell divides, and new cells are formed
50	• In a eukaryotic cell, structures in the nucleus that are made up of DNA and protein	• In a prokaryotic cell, the main ring of DNA	• Melanoma is a form of this.
100	• Human body cells have 46 of these.	• This process is different in animals and plants	• The DNA of a cell is organized into these structures.
200	• During the first stage of this, the cell grows and copies its organelles and chromosomes.	• It is during this process that the chromatids separate.	• This is uncontrolled cell division.
500	• The complicated process of separating chromosomes	• During this process, a cell plate forms in cells that have a cell wall.	• The cytoplasm splits in two during this process.

SECTION SUMMARY
Read the following section summary.

The life cycle of a cell is the cell cycle.

A cell copies its chromosomes during interphase.

Mitosis produces two nuclei that have the same number of chromosomes.

Mitosis has four phases: prophase, metaphase, anaphase, and telophase.

After mitosis, the cytoplasm is divided by cytokinesis into two daughter cells.

In plant cells, a cell plate forms between the two new cells during cytokinesis.

Cancer is a disorder of cell division.

Name _____ Class _____ Date _____

Skills Worksheet

Directed Reading B

Section: Mendel and His Peas (pp. 174–179)

1. What is heredity?

_____

_____

_____

2. What field of study did Mendel's experiments help establish?

_____

_____

BEFORE MENDEL

_____ **3.** If a brown rabbit mates with a white rabbit, the offspring would be tan according to the idea of
  a. mixing inheritance.
  b. proportionate inheritance.
  c. Mendelian inheritance.
  d. blending inheritance.

GREGOR MENDEL'S WORK

_____ **4.** Gregor Mendel was born in
  a. the United States.
  b. Austria.
  c. Germany.
  d. Italy.

5. Why did Mendel study garden peas?

_____

_____

6. Why is it possible for pea plants to self-pollinate?

_____

_____

_____

Directed Reading B continued

Match the correct definition with the correct term. Write the letter in the space provided.

_____ **7.** Pollen from one plant is carried by animals or wind to fertilize eggs in the ovule of another plant.

_____ **8.** Sperm from one plant fertilizes the eggs of the same plant.

_____ **9.** Egg and sperm from the same plant combine; all the offspring have the same traits as the parent.

a. self-pollination

b. true breeding

c. cross-pollination

10. If a plant that is true breeding for purple flowers self-pollinates and has offspring, what color will the flowers of the offspring be?

_____

11. A feature, such as hair color, that has different forms in a population is called

a(n) _____.

12. A different form of a characteristic, such as brown hair, is called

a(n) _____.

13. Besides flower color, what are three characteristics of pea plants that Mendel studied?

_____

_____

_____

14. Why did Mendel use plants that were true breeding for each of the traits he was studying?

_____

_____

15. When he crossed two pea plants that had different traits of the same characteristic, how was Mendel able to select which plants would be crossed to produce offspring?

_____

_____

_____

MENDEL'S FIRST EXPERIMENTS

_____ **16.** When plants that are true breeding for different traits of a
characteristic are crossed, the offspring are called
    a. dominant plants.
    b. recessive plants.
    c. first-generation plants.
    d. second-generation plants.

_____ **17.** When plants that are true breeding for different traits of a
characteristic are crossed, the trait observed in the first generation
is called the
    a. dominant trait.
    b. recessive trait.
    c. first-generation trait.
    d. second-generation trait.

_____ **18.** A trait that reappears in the second generation after disappearing in
the first generation is called a
    a. dominant trait.
    b. recessive trait.
    c. first-generation trait.
    d. second-generation trait.

MENDEL'S SECOND EXPERIMENTS

_____ **19.** When first-generation plants are allowed to self-pollinate, the offspring
are called
    a. dominant plants.
    b. recessive plants.
    c. first-generation plants.
    d. second-generation plants.

_____ **20.** When first-generation plants are allowed to self-pollinate, what type of
traits appear in the second generation?
    a. Only the dominant traits appear.
    b. Only the recessive traits appear.
    c. Dominant and recessive traits appear.
    d. New traits appear.

_____ **21.** In Mendel's experiments, what type of trait appeared most often in the
second generation?
    a. dominant traits
    b. recessive traits
    c. passive traits
    d. new traits

_____ **22.** A relationship between two different numbers that is often expressed
as a fraction is a(n)
   a. ratio.
   b. multiplier.
   c. sum.
   d. divisor.

_____ **23.** Mendel's results showed that the ratio of dominant traits to recessive
traits in second-generation plants is about
   a. 4:1.
   b. 3:1.
   c. 1:4.
   d. 1:3.

24. How did Mendel believe his results in calculating the ratio of dominant traits
to recessive traits could be explained?

_____

_____

25. If offspring receive two sets of instructions for each characteristic, how are
the offspring's traits determined?

_____

_____

26. How long after his results were published in 1865 was Mendel's work widely
recognized?

_____

Skills Worksheet

Directed Reading B

Section: Traits and Inheritance (pp. 180–187)
A GREAT IDEA

_____ 1. One set of instructions for an inherited trait is a(n)
   a. allele.
   b. phenotype.
   c. genotype.
   d. gene.

_____ 2. How many sets of the same gene for every characteristic do offspring receive?
   a. one from one parent
   b. one from each parent
   c. two from one parent
   d. two from each parent

_____ 3. One of the alternative forms of a gene that governs a characteristic is a(n)
   a. allele.
   b. phenotype.
   c. genotype.
   d. trait.

_____ 4. Dominant alleles are shown with
   a. capital letters.
   b. lowercase letters.
   c. boldface letters.
   d. italic letters.

_____ 5. Lowercase letters are used to show
   a. dominant alleles.
   b. recessive alleles.
   c. dominant genes.
   d. recessive genes.

_____ 6. An organism's appearance or other detectable characteristic is its
   a. genotype.
   b. phenotype.
   c. allele.
   d. trait.

_____ **7.** The entire genetic makeup of an organism, and the combination of genes for one or more specific traits, is an organism's
a. genotype. **c.** allele.
b. phenotype. **d.** trait.

_____ **8.** A plant with two dominant or two recessive alleles is said to be
a. homologous.
b. homozygous.
c. heterologous.
d. heterozygous.

_____ **9.** A plant with one dominant and one recessive allele is said to be
a. homologous.
b. homozygous.
c. heterologous.
d. heterozygous.

_____ **10.** For a particular cross, a Punnett square is used to predict
a. possible phenotypes of offspring.
b. possible genotypes of offspring.
c. possible phenotypes of parents.
d. possible genotypes of parents.

he Punnett square below shows a cross between a true-breeding purple flower
PP) and a true-breeding white flower (*pp*). Use the Punnett square to answer
questions 11 through 13.

	p	*p*
P	Pp	Pp
P	Pp	Pp

11. What is the genotype for the offspring of this cross?

_____

12. Why do all offspring from this cross have the same genotype?

_____

13. What color will the flowers of the offspring of this cross be? Explain your answer.

_____

_____

Directed Reading B *continued*

The allele for purple flowers (*P*) is dominant, and the allele for white flowers (*p*) is recessive. The Punnett square below shows a self-pollination cross of a plant with the genotype *Pp*. Use the Punnett square to answer questions 14 through 17.

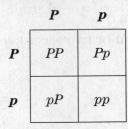

14. According to the Punnett square, what are the four possible genotypes for the offspring of this cross?

_____

15. Of the four possible genotypes for the offspring of the cross shown by the Punnett square, which two are exactly the same?

_____

16. What are the possible phenotypes for the offspring of this cross? Explain your answer.

_____

_____

17. What is the ratio of dominant to recessive traits for the offspring of this cross?

_____

WHAT ARE THE CHANCES?

_____ **18.** The mathematical chance that something will happen is called a(n)
   a. ratio.
   b. possibility.
   c. probability.
   d. trait.

_____ **19.** Probability is most often written as a(n)
   a. product or percentage.
   b. whole number or sum.
   c. whole number or equation.
   d. fraction or percentage.

_____ **20.** In a coin toss, what is the probability of tossing tails?
- **a.** 1/1
- **b.** 1/2
- **c.** 2/2
- **d.** 2/1

_____ **21.** In a coin toss, what calculation is used to find the probability that you will toss two heads in a row?
- **a.** $1/1 \times 1/1 = 1$
- **b.** $1/2 \times 1/2 = 1/4$
- **c.** $2/2 \times 2/2 = 4/4$
- **d.** $2/1 \times 2/1 = 4/1$

_____ **22.** In a $Pp \times Pp$ cross, what is the probability that offspring will inherit two p alleles?
- **a.** 1/4, or 25%
- **b.** 1/2, or 50%
- **c.** 3/4, or 75%
- **d.** 1/1, or 100%

23. Why were the traits Mendel examined in pea plants easy to predict?

_____

_____

MORE ABOUT TRAITS

_____ **24.** Eye color and fur color in a white tiger are controlled by
- **a.** one gene.
- **b.** two genes.
- **c.** many genes.
- **d.** one allele.

_____ **25.** Traits such as the color of skin, hair, and eyes result from
- **a.** one gene acting alone.
- **b.** one allele from each parent acting together.
- **c.** several genes acting together.
- **d.** one dominant allele.

26. Besides genes, what else can have an influence on traits?

_____

_____

Directed Reading B *continued*

27. Give one example of an internal environmental condition and one example of an external environmental condition that can affect an organism's phenotype.

_____

_____

_____

_____

GENETIC VARIATION

28. How many genes do scientists estimate humans have?

_____

29. The difference in the sets of alleles between individuals in a population is

called _____.

30. What is one example of genetic variation found in a population of corn snakes?

_____

_____

_____

31. What is an example of a trait inside your body that is affected by genes?

_____

_____

Skills Worksheet

Directed Reading B

Section: Meiosis (pp. 188–193)

1. In asexual reproduction, why do offspring have the same genotype as the parent?

_____

_____

2. Before sexual reproduction can occur, what must happen to the genetic material from each parent?

_____

_____

3. Genetic information is located on structures called _____.

CHROMOSOME NUMBERS

_____ **4.** Human body cells usually have
    a. 20 chromosomes.
    b. 23 chromosomes.
    c. 46 chromosomes.
    d. 78 chromosomes.

_____ **5.** In body cells, pairs of chromosomes that have the same sequence of genes and the same structure are called
    a. homozygous chromosomes.
    b. homologous chromosomes.
    c. diploid chromosomes.
    d. haploid chromosomes.

_____ **6.** Alleles for genes carried on homologous chromosomes are
    a. always the same.
    b. always different.
    c. never the same.
    d. sometimes different.

CHROMOSOMES IN REPRODUCTION

_____ **7.** Cells with homologous pairs of chromosomes are called
    a. homozygous cells.
    b. homologous cells.
    c. diploid cells.
    d. haploid cells.

Directed Reading B *continued*

_____ **8.** Before an organism can reproduce sexually, it must make
   a. diploid cells.
   b. sex cells.
   c. proteins.
   d. homologous cells.

9. Why don't sex cells have homologous pairs of chromosomes?

_____

_____

10. Cells that do not have homologous pairs of chromosomes are

called _____ cells.

11. What kind of cell is formed when chromosomes from a sperm cell and an egg cell combine?

_____

MEIOSIS

_____ **12.** A process in cell division that produces cells that have half the usual number of chromosomes is called
   a. meiosis.
   b. mitosis.
   c. fertilization.
   d. pollination.

_____ **13.** Human egg cells have
   a. 46 chromosomes.
   b. 23 chromosomes.
   c. 10 chromosomes.
   d. 1 chromosome.

_____ **14.** The new cell that forms when human egg and sperm cells join has
   a. 46 chromosomes.
   b. 23 chromosomes.
   c. 10 chromosomes.
   d. 1 chromosome.

Match the labels to the illustrations showing the first division during meiosis. Write the letters in the space provided.

 a. 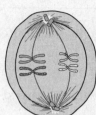 b. 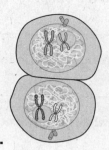 c.  d.

_____ **15.** Chromosomes are copied before meiosis begins, and the chromatids are joined together.

_____ **16.** Pairs of homologous chromosomes line up along the equator of the cell.

_____ **17.** Homologous chromosomes separate and move to opposite ends of the cell.

_____ **18.** Nuclear membrane re-forms; the cell divides.

Match the labels to the illustrations showing the second division during meiosis. Write the letters in the space provided.

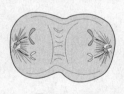 a.   b.   c.   d.

_____ **19.** Two cells contain one member of the homologous chromosome pair.

_____ **20.** Chromosomes line up along the equator of each cell.

_____ **21.** Chromatids pull apart and move to opposite ends of the cell; nuclear membrane re-forms; cell divides.

_____ **22.** Four new haploid cells form; each new cell has half the number of chromosomes present in the original cell.

23. If a male plant that is true breeding for the recessive trait for wrinkled seeds is crossed with a female plant that is true breeding for the dominant trait for round seeds, what shape will the offspring's seeds have? Explain why.

_____

24. How much of an offspring's genetic material is contributed by each parent?

_____

25. Outside the nucleus, what is one structure where genetic material is stored in an animal cell?

_____

26. Why is the mitochondrial DNA in the cells of offspring the same as the mitochondrial DNA in the offspring's mother?

_____

_____

Name _____ Class _____ Date _____

Vocabulary and Section Summary B

Mendel and His Peas

VOCABULARY

After you finish reading the section, try this puzzle! Use the clues below to write the word or phrase in the appropriate spaces.

1. the passing of genetic traits from parents to offspring

___ ___ ___ ___ ___ ___ ___ ___
     2

2. a feature that has different forms in a population

___ ___ ___ ___ ___ ___ ___ ___ ___ ___ ___ ___ ___ ___ ___
                5   7

3. a trait that reappears in the second generation after disappearing in the first generation

___ ___ ___ ___ ___ ___ ___ ___ ___ ___ ___ ___ ___ ___
          11

4. a relationship between two different numbers

___ ___ ___ ___ ___
    10

5. the trait observed in the first generation when parents that have different traits are bred

___ ___ ___ ___ ___ ___ ___ ___ ___ ___ ___ ___
  4   1

6. when sperm from one plant fertilizes the eggs of the same plant

___ ___ ___ ___ ___ – ___ ___ ___ ___ ___ ___ ___ ___
        8   6

7. a plant that, when it self-pollinates, will have offspring with the same trait as the parent

___ ___ ___ ___ ___ – ___ ___ ___ ___ ___ ___ ___
    9   3

Using the numbered letters above, fill in the spaces below to find a phrase related to heredity.

8. ___ ___ ___ ___ ___ ___ ___ , ___ ___ ___ ___
   1 2 3 4 5 6   7   8 9 10 11

SECTION SUMMARY

Read the following section summary

- Heredity is the passing of traits from parents to offspring.
- Before Mendel's ideas were accepted, people explained inheritance as the blending of traits from each parent.
- Gregor Mendel's experiments using pea plants eventually changed the way people thought about heredity.
- When parents with different traits are bred, dominant traits are always present in the first generation. Recessive traits are not visible in the first generation but reappear in the second generation.
- Mendel found a 3:1 ratio of dominant-to-recessive traits in the second generation.
- Mendel's ideas are the foundation of modern genetics.

Skills Worksheet

Vocabulary and Section Summary B

Traits and Inheritance
VOCABULARY

After you finish reading the section, try this puzzle! In the space provided, write the term described. Then, find the words in the word search puzzle below. Terms can be hidden in the puzzle vertically, horizontally, diagonally, or backward.

_____ 1. the likelihood that a possible future event will occur in any given instance of the event

_____ 2. one of the alternative forms of a gene that governs a characteristic

_____ 3. one set of instructions for an inherited trait

_____ 4. the entire genetic makeup of an organism

_____ 5. an organism's appearance or other detectable characteristic

A	H	T	I	C	L	D	T	B	O	F	Y	A	I	E
E	G	N	H	A	R	Y	P	V	W	T	S	G	Y	S
U	E	A	L	P	H	E	N	O	T	Y	P	E	E	T
E	H	L	A	T	E	I	E	N	A	R	I	N	A	S
A	E	D	H	L	P	E	B	C	D	B	H	E	N	W
K	T	G	F	K	L	T	B	Y	P	O	D	P	R	E
F	B	I	B	H	G	E	N	O	T	Y	P	E	G	B
G	E	M	A	L	O	F	L	L	E	I	I	Y	L	P
I	A	N	Y	C	D	Z	G	E	O	B	F	D	E	R
D	T	O	V	O	T	E	I	V	H	A	C	B	W	O
E	P	Y	T	I	L	I	B	A	B	O	R	P	A	Y
I	A	P	H	D	U	C	M	B	L	A	Y	E	E	D
C	N	J	M	R	E	S	U	S	U	I	C	L	L	E

Vocabulary and Section Summary B *continued*

SECTION SUMMARY

Read the following section summary

- Instructions for an inherited trait are called *genes*. For each gene, there are two alleles, one inherited from each parent. Both alleles make up an organism's genotype.

- An organism's phenotype is the organism's observable characteristics.

- Punnett squares show all possible offspring genotypes.

- Probability can be used to describe possible outcomes in offspring and the likelihood of each outcome.

- Some genes influence more than one trait.

- Some traits are influenced by many genes.

- The environment can influence how genes are expressed.

- Scientists estimate that humans have approximately 30,000 genes.

Vocabulary and Section Summary B

Meiosis

VOCABULARY

After you finish reading the section, try this puzzle! Use the clues below to unscramble the letters. Then, write the word or phrase in the space provided.

1. a cell that contains two haploid sets of chromosomes: IOPDDLI

_____

2. a process in cell division during which the number of chromosomes decreases to half the original number: OIESMSI

_____

3. male sex cells: PRSEM

_____

4. have the same sequence of genes and the same structure: GOOUSHMLOO MSOOSHCORME

_____

5. a cell, nucleus, or organism that has only one set of unpaired chromosomes: PLADOIH

_____

6. female sex cell: GEG

_____

SECTION SUMMARY

Read the following section summary

Homologous pairs of chromosomes contain the same genes. The alleles for each gene may be the same or they may be different.

Diploid cells have homologous pairs of chromosomes. Haploid cells do not.

The process of meiosis produces haploid sex cells.

During sexual reproduction, haploid sex cells combine to form a new diploid organism.

Meiosis explains how organisms inherit one-half of their genetic information from each parent.

Skills Worksheet

Directed Reading B

Section: What Does DNA Look Like? (pp. 208–211)

_____ 1. Inherited characteristics are determined by
   a. genes.
   b. traits.
   c. molecules.
   d. environment.

_____ 2. Structures made of protein and DNA and found in the nucleus of cells are called
   a. inherited characteristics.
   b. phosphates.
   c. nucleotides.
   d. chromosomes.

_____ 3. What is another way to say deoxyribonucleic acid?
   a. DRA
   b. DBA
   c. DXA
   d. DNA

4. What is *DNA*?

_____

_____

_____

THE PIECES OF THE PUZZLE

_____ 5. The subunits that make up DNA are called
   a. genes.
   b. nucleotides.
   c. chromosomes.
   d. cells.

6. What two things must the material that makes up genes be able to do?

_____

_____

_____

7. Why must genes be copied each time a cell divides?

_____

_____

_____

8. What allows the genetic material for genes to give instructions and be copied before a cell divides?

_____

9. What does a nucleotide in a nucleic acid chain consist of?

_____

_____

_____

10. What are the four bases of a nucleotide in DNA?

_____

_____

_____

11. What do the four letters scientists often use to refer to the bases of nucleotides stand for?

_____

_____

Match the correct description with the correct term. Write the letter in the space provided.

_____ 12. found that adenine is always equal to thymine, and guanine is always equal to cytosine in DNA

_____ 13. used X rays to make images of the DNA molecule, suggesting that DNA has a spiral shape

_____ 14. built a model of DNA that helped explain how DNA is copied and functions

a. Rosalind Franklin
b. Watson and Crick
c. Erwin Chargaff

DNA'S DOUBLE STRUCTURE

_____ **15.** The twisted shape of DNA is called a
  a. double ladder.
  b. double helix.
  c. nucleotide.
  d. base pair.

_____ **16.** The two sides of the double helix DNA ladder are made of alternating sugar parts and
  a. cytosine parts.
  b. base parts.
  c. thymine parts.
  d. phosphate parts.

_____ **17.** The rungs of the double helix DNA ladder are made of a pair of
  a. sugars.
  b. phosphates.
  c. bases.
  d. acids.

_____ **18.** When the base on one side of a DNA ladder rung is adenine, the other side of the rung is always
  a. thymine.
  b. guanine.
  c. cytosine.
  d. phosphate.

_____ **19.** When the base on one side of a DNA ladder rung is guanine, the other side of the rung is always
  a. thymine.
  b. guanine.
  c. cytosine.
  d. phosphate.

20. When Chargaff separated the parts of a sample of DNA, what did he find out about the matching bases?

_____

_____

21. What did Watson and Crick learn about the fit of the correct pairs of bases within the width of the DNA ladder?

_____

_____

Directed Reading B *continued*

DNA REPLICATION

22. The pairing of bases allows the cell to _____, or make copies of DNA.

23. In a DNA molecule, pairs of bases are _____ to each other, since each base always bonds with only one other base.

24. In a DNA molecule, what base sequence is complementary to the sequence CGAC?

_____

25. In what direction does a DNA molecule split during replication?

_____

26. As a DNA molecule splits, what is added to the exposed bases on the original molecule?

_____

27. What happens to DNA every time a cell divides?

_____

28. In the cell, what does the job of unwinding, copying, and rewinding the DNA?

_____

Skills Worksheet

Directed Reading B

Section: How DNA Works (pp. 212–217)

1. How much DNA does a single cell in your body hold?

_____

_____

UNRAVELING DNA

2. What makes up a chromosome?

_____

3. What is chromatin?

_____

4. What happens to DNA to make it fit inside a cell?

_____

5. What forms the code that carries information for DNA?

_____

6. A string of nucleotides that give the cell information about a certain trait is

known as a(n) _____.

7. Describe the genetic material contained in each of the 46 chromosomes of a human cell just before division.

_____

_____

8. Describe the chromatids that make up a chromosome when a cell is ready to divide.

_____

_____

GENES AND PROTEINS

_____ **9.** How are the codes for specific amino acids formed?
   a. with groups of three bases
   b. with groups of four bases
   c. with a pair of bases
   d. with groups of proteins

_____ **10.** A long string of amino acids forms a
    a. nucleotide.
    b. cell.
    c. trait.
    d. protein.

_____ **11.** A set of instructions for making a particular protein is a(n)
    a. nucleotide.
    b. amino acid.
    c. gene.
    d. chromosome.

_____ **12.** The chemical triggers and messengers for many processes within cells are
    a. mutagens.
    b. chromatids.
    c. ribosomes.
    d. proteins.

_____ **13.** How many genes that code for proteins does a single organism typically have?
    a. hundreds
    b. thousands
    c. hundreds of thousands
    d. millions

_____ **14.** A molecule present in all living cells that plays a role in protein production is
    a. RBA.
    b. RUA.
    c. RCA.
    d. RNA.

_____ **15.** The base that replaces thymine in RNA is called
    a. adenine.
    b. guanine.
    c. uracil.
    d. cytosine.

16. What two forms of RNA work with ribosomes to make proteins?

_____

_____

Match the correct description with the correct term. Write the letter in the space provided.

_____ 17. a mirrorlike copy of one side of the segment of DNA containing a gene

_____ 18. the "factory" in the cytoplasm where a new protein molecule is made

_____ 19. molecules that pick up specific amino acids from the cytoplasm, whose bases match up with bases on messenger RNA

_____ 20. molecule formed when amino acids released by transfer RNA link then fold up

a. ribosome

b. messenger RNA

c. protein

d. transfer RNA

CHANGES IN GENES

_____ 21. A change in the nucleotide-base sequence of a gene or DNA molecule is called a(n)
   a. mutagen.
   b. mutation.
   c. antigen.
   d. chromatid.

_____ 22. Random errors when DNA is copied are called
   a. mutagens.
   b. mutations.
   c. antigens.
   d. chromatids.

_____ 23. A physical or chemical agent that can cause a mutation in DNA is called a(n)
   a. mutagen.
   b. protein.
   c. antigen.
   d. chromatid.

24. What is one example of a mutation that causes an improved trait?

_____

_____

25. Why do some mutations cause no changes to a trait?

_____

_____

26. What is one example of a mutation that produces a harmful trait?

_____

_____

27. What kinds of traits are produced by most mutations?

_____

28. What happens to a gene if a mutation occurs in sex cells?

_____

_____

_____

Skills Worksheet

Vocabulary and Section Summary B

What Does DNA Look Like?

VOCABULARY

After you finish reading the section, try this puzzle! Use the clues below to complete the crossword puzzle.

ACROSS

4. pairs with cytosine

7. made of protein and DNA

9. pairs with guanine

10. process used to make images of DNA (two words)

DOWN

1. pairs with thymine

2. shape of DNA (two words)

3. pairs with adenine

5. to copy DNA

6. subunit of DNA made from sugar, phosphate, and a base

8. genetic material of living things

SECTION SUMMARY

Read the following section summary.

DNA is the material that makes up genes.

Investigations by Chargaff, Franklin, Watson, and Crick led to the discovery of DNA's structure and function.

The DNA molecule looks like a twisted ladder, or double helix. The two halves are long strings of nucleotides.

In DNA, adenine always pairs with thymine, and guanine always pairs with cytosine.

The structure of DNA allows it to be replicated accurately.

Skills Worksheet

Vocabulary and Section Summary B

How DNA Works
VOCABULARY

After you finish reading the section, try this puzzle! Using the clues, unscramble the letters to fill in the blanks. Then, using the final clue, fill in the boxes to unravel the secret message.

1. molecule that helps build new proteins by copying DNA: ANR

   ___ ___ ___

2. long strands of DNA and protein: MAHCTNIOR

   ___ ___ ___ ___ ___ ___ ___ ___ ___
       7

3. organelle composed of RNA and protein: MOOSERIB

   ___ ___ ___ ___ ___ ___ ___ ___
        4   2

4. string of nucleotides that gives the cell information about how to make a specific trait: NEGE

   ___ ___ ___ ___

5. nucleotide base known as U: CLIRUA

   ___ ___ ___ ___ ___ ___
           9

6. change in the nucleotide-base sequence: NUTATOMI

   ___ ___ ___ ___ ___ ___ ___ ___
        10

7. copy of the DNA segment: NRGSESEME NRA

   ___ ___ ___ ___ ___ ___ ___ ___ ___ ___ ___ ___
           6

8. physical or chemical agent that can cause a mutation: GTEAMUN

   ___ ___ ___ ___ ___ ___ ___
     3

9. molecules that translate the RNA message: FTERASNR NAR

   ___ ___ ___ ___ ___ ___ ___ ___ ___ ___ ___
         8

10. Fill in the missing letters and finish the secret message.

D				L	
1	2	3	4	5	6

				X
7	8	9	10	11

SECTION SUMMARY

Read the following section summary.

A gene is a set of instructions for making a protein. DNA stores these genetic instructions.

Every organism has DNA in its cells. Humans have about 2 m of DNA in each cell.

Traits of organisms are typically determined by proteins, which are coded for by segments of DNA called genes.

Within a gene, each group of three bases codes for one amino acid. A sequence of amino acids is linked to make a protein.

Proteins are built within the cytoplasm of cells.

A mutation is a change in the DNA that can affect the traits of an organism.

Skills Worksheet

Directed Reading B

Section: The Study of Earth's History (pp. 234–237)
THE EARLY STUDY OF GEOLOGY

_____ 1. Who is responsible for outlining the principle now called
uniformitarianism?
a. Albert Einstein
b. James Hurst
c. James Hutton
d. Charles Lyell

_____ 2. The principle of uniformitarianism states that
a. the geologic processes once at work are now changing.
b. Earth changes only at certain times and only after certain events.
c. Earth is uniform and unchanging; it has always been as it is now.
d. the same geologic processes have been at work throughout Earth's
history.

_____ 3. Which of the following processes was NOT observed by Hutton when
he developed the idea of uniformitarianism?
a. Rivers carry rock particles upstream.
b. In time, new rock will be raised and create new landforms.
c. Rock particles are deposited and form new layers of sediment.
d. Rock is broken down into smaller particles.

**Match the correct description with the correct term. Write the letter in the space
provided.**

_____ 4. the principle that states that past geologic
processes can be explained by current
geologic processes

_____ 5. the principle that states that geologic change
occurs suddenly

_____ 6. rare, sudden events that cause change

_____ 7. the author of *Theory of the Earth*

_____ 8. the author of *Principles of Geology*

a. James Hutton

b. catastrophism

c. Charles Lyell

d. catastrophes

e. uniformitarianism

MODERN GEOLOGY—A HAPPY MEDIUM

9. During the late 20th century, scientists challenged uniformitarianism again. What do these scientists believe about catastrophes?

_____

_____

_____

10. What present-day evidence suggests that the extinction of dinosaurs was the result of a catastrophic event?

_____

_____

_____

PALEONTOLOGY—THE STUDY OF PAST LIFE

Match the correct definition with the correct term. Write the letter in the space provided.

_____ **11.** the study of past life using fossils

_____ **12.** scientists who study past life using fossils

_____ **13.** remains of organisms preserved by geologic processes

a. paleontology

b. fossils

c. paleontologists

Skills Worksheet

Directed Reading B

Section: Relative Dating (pp. 238–245)

_____ 1. Determining the age of objects or events in relation to other objects or events is called
a. relative sequencing.
b. relative dating.
c. relative history.
d. relative geology.

THE ROCK CYCLE

Match the correct description with the correct term. Write the letter in the space provided.

_____ 2. forms from rock fragments

_____ 3. forms when magma cools

_____ 4. forms when solid rock changes to another type of rock due to temperature or pressure changes

a. igneous rock
b. metamorphic rock
c. sedimentary rock

Match the correct description with the correct term. Write the letter in the space provided.

_____ 5. Sediment is hardened into sedimentary rock.

_____ 6. This moves sediment from one place to another.

_____ 7. Rock is broken down into smaller pieces.

_____ 8. Material is laid down or dropped.

a. weathering
b. erosion
c. deposition
d. lithification

THE PRINCIPLE OF SUPERPOSITION

_____ 9. As long as a sequence of rock layers is undisturbed, scientists know that
a. older rocks lie above younger rocks.
b. younger rocks lie below older rocks.
c. younger rocks lie above older rocks.
d. older rocks have eroded away.

_____ **10.** The principle that states that younger rocks lie above older rocks in undisturbed sequences is called
  a. relative dating.
  b. superposition.
  c. uniformitarianism.
  d. catastrophism.

DISTURBED ROCK LAYERS

Match the correct description with the correct term. Write the letter in the space provided.

_____ **11.** a break in Earth's crust along which blocks of crust slide relative to one another

_____ **12.** younger sediment deposited on top of older layers

_____ **13.** molten rock that has squeezed into existing rock and hardened

_____ **14.** rock layers bent and buckled by Earth's internal forces

_____ **15.** rock layers slanted by Earth's internal forces but without folding

a. superposition
b. folding
c. fault
d. tilting
e. intrusion

16. When a layer or several layers of rock are missing from a rock-layer

sequence, this is called a(n) _____.

17. Name two possible explanations for a missing layer in a rock-layer sequence.

_____

_____

18. An unconformity is created when an area is uplifted and exposed to

_____ by wind and water.

ROCK-LAYER PUZZLES

19. Why is a crosscutting feature always younger than the rock layers it cuts across?

_____

_____

_____

20. How do geologists figure out rock-layer puzzles?

_____

_____

_____

_____

ORDER OF EVENTS

21. Geologists use superposition and crosscutting relationships to find what?

_____

22. Can relative dating tell geologists exactly when events took place? Explain your answer.

_____

_____

Skills Worksheet

Directed Reading B

Section: Absolute Dating (pp. 246–249)

1. What is the purpose of absolute dating?

_____

_____

RADIOACTIVE DECAY

2. Atoms of the same element that have the same number of protons but a

different number of neutrons are called _____.

3. When an isotope is _____, it does not undergo
radioactive decay.

4. When an isotope is _____, it is called radioactive.

5. During _____, an unstable isotope breaks down into
a stable isotope.

6. How do scientists use isotopes to determine the age of an object?

_____

_____

_____

7. An unstable isotope is called a(n) _____ isotope.

8. The stable isotope is called the _____ isotope.

9. The more daughter material there is in a rock sample, the

_____ the rock is.

10. Determining the age of a sample based on the ratio of parent material to

daughter material is called _____.

11. The time it takes for one-half of a radioactive sample to decay is called

a(n) _____.

12. After every half-life, what has happened to the parent material in an object?

_____

_____

_____

13. The best types of rock samples to use for radiometric dating

are _____ rocks.

USING RADIOMETRIC DATING

14. To date the age of our solar system, scientists perform radiometric dating

on moon rocks and _____.

Match the correct description with the correct term. Write the letter in the space provided.

_____ **15.** used mainly for dating rocks older than 100,000 years

_____ **16.** used to date rocks older than 10 million years; half-life of isotope is 4.5 billion years

a. potassium-argon

b. uranium-lead

Name _____ Class _____ Date _____

Vocabulary and Section Summary B

The Study of Earth's History
VOCABULARY

After you finish reading the section, try this puzzle! Use the clues given to fill in the blanks below. Then, copy the numbered letters into the corresponding boxes below to answer the bonus question.

1. the remains of organisms preserved by geologic processes

— — — — — — — —
    6

2. the study of past life

— — — — — — — — — — — — — —
10   2 5   16   7

3. the theory that today's geologic processes have been at work throughout Earth's history

— — — — — — — — — — — — — — — — —
  8   14   13

4. the theory that geologic change happens suddenly

— — — — — — — — — —
9   11   17   1

5. scientists who study past life

— — — — — — — — — — — — —
  12   15   3 4

6. What do modern geologists believe shaped Earth's surface?

— — — **W** — — — — — — — —
1 2 3   4 5 6 7 3 4 8 9

— — — — — — — — — — — **D**
10 11 3 9 12 13 1 12 13 14 15

— — — — — — — — — — —
9 14 16 14 1 16 11 6 10 17 8 9

— **V** — — — —
12 5 15 16 1

SECTION SUMMARY

Read the following section summary.

- Uniformitarianism assumes that geologic change is gradual. Catastrophism is based on the idea that geologic change is sudden.

- Modern geology is based on the idea that gradual geologic change is interrupted by catastrophes.

- Using fossils to study past life is called paleontology.

Skills Worksheet

Vocabulary and Section Summary B

Relative Dating
VOCABULARY

After you finish reading the section, try this puzzle! The underlined words below are missing all their vowels. Write the completed words in the spaces provided.

1. According to the <u>LW F CRSSCTTNG RLTNSHPS</u>, a fault or body of rock is younger than any other body of rock it cuts through.

_____

2. <u>SDMNTRY RCK</u> forms from compressed or cemented fragments of other rocks.

_____

3. <u>SPRPSTN</u> states that older rocks lie below younger rocks in undisturbed sequences.

_____

4. Scientists use <u>RLTV DTNG</u> to determine whether objects are older or younger than other objects.

_____

5. A(n) <u>NCNFRMTY</u> is created when deposition stops or erosion occurs.

_____

SECTION SUMMARY

Read the following section summary.

Geologists use relative dating to determine the order in which events happen.

The rock cycle describes processes that form and recycle rock on Earth.

Sedimentary rock forms when layers of sediment are lithified. Fossils may be preserved in sedimentary rock.

The principle of superposition states that in undisturbed rock sequences, younger sedimentary rock layers lie above older layers.

Folding and tilting are two events that disturb rock layers. Faults and intrusions are two features that cut across rock layers.

Unconformities occur when rock layers are eroded or when sediment is not deposited for a long time.

The law of crosscutting relationships states that structures and features that cut across rock layers are younger than the rock layers.

Superposition and crosscutting relationships allow geologists to determine the order in which rock layers and features form but not the age in years of rock layers and features.

Vocabulary and Section Summary B

Absolute Dating
VOCABULARY

After you finish reading the section, try this puzzle! Use the clues below to solve the crossword puzzle.

ACROSS

3. same number of protons, different number of neutrons

4. based on the ratio of parent isotopes to daughter isotopes (two words)

6. rocks that have traveled through space to earth

7. time needed for one-half of a radioactive sample to decay

8. measuring the age of an event or object in years (two words)

DOWN

1. an unstable and radioactive isotope

2. breakdown of an unstable isotope into a stable isotope (two words)

5. stable isotope produced through decay

SECTION SUMMARY

Read the following section summary.

During radioactive decay, an unstable isotope decays and becomes a stable isotope of the same element or a different element.

Radiometric dating, based on the ratio of parent to daughter material, is used to determine the absolute age of a sample.

The method of radiometric dating is chosen based on the estimated age of the sample.

Earth and the solar system are about 4.6 billion years old.

Name _____ Class _____ Date _____

Directed Reading B

Section: Looking at Fossils (pp. 264–269)
FOSSILIZED ORGANISMS

_____ 1. The trace or remains of an organism that lived long ago, most commonly preserved in sedimentary rock, is a
  a. rock.
  b. fossil.
  c. meteorite.
  d. trace element.

2. Describe how organisms are preserved in sedimentary rock.

_____

_____

_____

3. Soft, sticky tree sap that can trap insects, frogs, and lizards, then harden

  is called _____.

4. Why are many frozen fossils preserved from the last ice age?

_____

_____

_____

5. How long have the La Brea asphalt deposits preserved trapped organisms?

_____

6. The process in which minerals replace the pore space in an organism's hard

  tissue, or all an organism's tissues, is called _____.

OTHER TYPES OF FOSSILS

7. What is a trace fossil?

_____

_____

_____

Match the correct definition with the correct term. Write the letter in the space provided.

_____ **8.** trace fossil that can show how big an animal was and how fast it was moving

_____ **9.** trace fossil formed by the shelter of an animal, such as a clam, that buries itself in sediment

_____ **10.** trace fossil formed from preserved animal dung

_____ **11.** the impression left in sediment or rock where a plant or animal was buried

_____ **12.** an object formed when sediment fills a mold and becomes rock

a. mold

b. coprolite

c. fooprint

d. cast

e. burrow

USING FOSSILS TO INTERPRET THE PAST

13. The history of life in the geologic past as indicated by the traces or remains of living things is the _____.

14. What are two reasons that the fossil record is incomplete?

_____

_____

15. In what kind of environment were marine fossils found on mountains in the Yoho National Park in Canada formed?

_____

16. How does fossil evidence of forests and freshwater organisms in Antarctica show that the climate there was warmer in the past?

_____

17. What are two things scientists compare to help them interpret how life has changed over time?

_____

DATING THE FOSSIL RECORD

_____ **18.** Compared to fossils of organisms that lived more recently, fossils of more ancient life forms are found
   a. in younger rock layers.
   b. in older rock layers.
   c. on top of rocks.
   d. in either young or old rock layers.

_____ **19.** How do scientists find out the age of an index fossil?
    a. They date only the rock layer above the fossil.
    b. They date only the rock layer below the fossil.
    c. They date the rock layers above and below the fossil.
    d. They compare the fossil to present-day organisms.

_____ **20.** Which of the following is NOT true of index fossils?
    a. They appear only in certain rock layers.
    b. They appear all over the world.
    c. They were organisms that lived during a short, well-defined geologic time span.
    d. They are hard to identify.

_____ **21.** What do scientists use index fossils for?
    a. to date the rock layers they are found in
    b. to learn about the ocean floor
    c. to learn about the minerals they are found in
    d. to learn what ancient organisms ate

22. About how old are the rock layers where fossils of *Phacops*, a kind of trilobite, are found? How do scientists know?

_____

_____

23. About how long ago did ammonites called *Tropites* live?

_____

Skills Worksheet

Directed Reading B

Section: Earth's Changing Continents (pp. 270–275)
PLATE TECTONICS

_____ 1. The theory that explains how Earth's tectonic plates move and change shape is called
    a. continental drift.
    b. tectonic drift.
    c. plate theory.
    d. plate tectonics.

2. The thin, cool "skin" of Earth is called the _____.

3. Tectonic plates rest on a thick layer of slowly moving, solid rock called

the _____.

4. How fast do tectonic plates move?

_____

5. Why can tectonic plates move thousands of miles?

_____

_____

Match the correct description with the correct term. Write the letter in the space provided

_____ 6. where two or more tectonic plates collide, separate, or grind past each other

_____ 7. where tectonic plates move toward each other

_____ 8. formed where plates of continental lithosphere are forced together, then crumple

_____ 9. formed where dense oceanic lithosphere sinks under continental lithosphere

_____ 10. where tectonic plates move apart

_____ 11. formed when plates move apart; can widen for millions of years to form a new ocean

_____ 12. where tectonic plates slide past each other horizontally

_____ 13. caused by the horizontal movement of plates in areas like the San Andreas fault

a. divergent boundary

b. transform boundary

c. mountain belt

d. earthquake

e. convergent boundary

f. rift

g. plate boundary

h. line of volcanoes

CONTINENTAL DRIFT

_____ **14.** The continents once formed a single landmass, broke up, and drifted to their present locations because of
    a. tectonic drift.
    b. plate tectonics.
    c. continental drift.
    d. continental tectonics.

_____ **15.** As a continent moves across Earth's surface,
    a. it carries oceans with it.
    b. it carries rocks and fossils with it.
    c. rocks and fossils fall off it.
    d. it carries lithosphere with it.

16. What evidence from rocks shows that India, South America, and Africa were part of a single landmass located near the South Pole about 280 million years ago?

_____

_____

_____

17. How does finding *Mesosaurus* fossils in South America and southwestern Africa show that the continents of South America and Africa were joined?

_____

_____

_____

HISTORY OF CONTINENTAL DRIFT

_____ **18.** About 245 million years ago, all of Earth's continents made up a supercontinent called
    a. Pandora.
    b. Godwanaland.
    c. Eurasia.
    d. Pangaea.

_____ **19.** Beginning about 200 million years ago, the supercontinent Pangea
    a. split into several new plates.
    b. joined with another supercontinent.
    c. was destroyed and reformed.
    d. began to be surrounded by a superocean.

_____ **20.** When Pangaea's new plates drifted apart and those new continents separated,

    a. a superocean formed between them.

    b. tectonic plates stopped moving between them.

    c. new continents formed between them.

    d. a new ocean formed between them.

21. What happened to rocks and fossils as the tectonic plates separated and drifted apart?

_____

_____

22. If continents moved toward the equator because of continental drift, what happened to their climates?

_____

_____

23. How did continental drift affect temperature and precipitation patterns around the planet?

_____

_____

_____

24. How did Antarctica become the icy land we see today?

_____

_____

_____

25. How does the theory of continental drift explain why different organisms live on different continents?

_____

_____

26. How does the theory of continental drift explain changes to sea life when new oceans formed?

_____

_____

_____

27. How does the theory of continental drift explain why fossils of the same organisms are found on different continents?

_____

_____

_____

CASE STUDY: THE PANAMA LAND BRIDGE

_____ **28.** About 3 million years ago, what narrow strip of land joined North and South America for the first time?

    a. the Panama Canal   **c.** the Pangaea Land Bridge

    b. the Island of Panama   **d.** the Panama Land Bridge

29. What are two types of animals that crossed the Panama Land Bridge from South America to North America?

_____

_____

30. What are two types of animals that crossed the Panama Land Bridge from North America to South America?

_____

_____

31. What happened to some populations of clams, snails, corals, and sea urchins that became separated by the Panama Land Bridge?

_____

_____

_____

32. How was the Gulf Stream formed?

_____

_____

_____

33. How was the climate of Western Europe affected by the Gulf Stream?

_____

_____

Name _____ Class _____ Date _____

Skills Worksheet

Directed Reading B

Section: Time Marches On (pp. 276–283)
THE GEOLOGIC TIME SCALE

_____ 1. About how many years of Earth's history do geologists study?
   a. 4.6 million years   **c.** 460 million years
   b. 46 million years   **d.** 4.6 billion years

2. What is the geologic time scale?

_____

_____

_____

Match the correct description with the correct term. Write the letter in the space provided.

_____ 3. the largest division of the geologic time scale   **a.** epoch

_____ 4. the second-largest division of geologic time   **b.** period

_____ 5. the third-largest division of geologic time   **c.** era

_____ 6. the smallest division of geologic time   **d.** eon

7. What are three ways the boundaries between geologic time intervals are defined?

_____

_____

_____

8. What are two types of changes that can cause a dramatic incease or decrease in the number of different kinds of organisms?

_____

_____

9. What is *extinction?*

_____

_____

_____

10. What are two types of gradual changes that can cause mass extinctions?

_____

_____

11. What is one type of catastrophic change that can cause a mass extinction?

_____

PRECAMBRIAN TIME—LIFE DEVELOPS

_____ **12.** About how long did the Precambrian time last?
  a. 4.6 billion years ago to 542 million years ago
  b. 542 million years ago to 251 million years ago
  c. 251 million years ago to 65 million years ago
  d. 65 million years ago to the present

_____ **13.** Organisms first appeared in Earth's oceans about
  a. 4.6 billion years ago   **c.** 542 million years ago
  b. 3.6 billion years ago   **d.** 4.6 million years ago

14. Oxygen gas was released into Earth's early oceans and air by

_____.

15. How did the formation of ozone in the upper atmosphere help life survive on land?

_____

_____

16. Organisms composed of many cells may have evolved from

_____.

THE PALEOZOIC ERA

_____ **17.** When did the Paleozoic Era begin?
  a. about 2.6 billion years ago   **c.** about 542 million years ago
  b. about 430 million years ago   **d.** about 4.5 million years ago

18. Why do scientists know less about organisms before the Paleozoic Era than about organisms during the Paleozoic Era?

_____

_____

_____

19. What was the Cambrian explosion?

_____

_____

_____

20. What are three types of marine animals that left fossils from the Paleozoic Era?

_____

_____

_____

21. What type of forests covered much of Earth at the end of the Paleozoic Era?

_____

22. What indicates that arthropods such as scorpions were the first land animals?

_____

23. What was the largest known mass extinction?

_____

24. What was the largest group of animals that became extinct during the Permian extinction?

_____

25. According to the fossil record, what are two groups of animals that survived the Permian extinction?

_____

_____

HE MESOZOIC ERA

_____ **26.** When did the Mesozoic Era begin?
   a. about 2.6 billion years ago
   b. about 251 million years ago
   c. about 542 million years ago
   d. about 430 million years ago

27. The Mesozoic Era is also known as the _____.

28. The best-known reptiles that lived during the Mesozoic Era

   are _____.

29. The most important plants during the early Mesozoic Era were

_____.

30. What happened during the Cretaceous-Tertiary extinction?

_____

_____

_____

31. What fossil evidence do scientists have for the Cretaceous-Tertiary extinction?

_____

_____

_____

32. How could an object from our solar system have caused the Cretaceous-Tertiary extinction?

_____

_____

_____

THE CENOZOIC ERA

_____ **33.** When did the Cenozoic Era end?
   a. 40 million years ago
   b. 3.6 million years ago
   c. 542 million years ago
   d. The Cenozoic Era has not ended.

_____ **34.** The Cenozoic Era is sometimes called the
   a. Age of Humans.
   b. Age of Fossils.
   c. Age of Mammals.
   d. Age of Insects.

_____ **35.** Mastodons, camels, horses, and humans first appeared
   a. during the Cenozoic Era.
   b. during the Mesozoic Era.
   c. during the Paleozoic Era.
   d. during the Archean Era.

Vocabulary and Section Summary B

Looking at Fossils

VOCABULARY

After you finish reading the section, try this puzzle! Use the clues to solve the crossword puzzle below.

ACROSS

1. an object that forms when sediment fills a mold and becomes a rock

4. hardened tree sap

6. the remains of an organism that lived during a relatively short, well-defined geologic time span

7. preserved animal dung

DOWN

2. any fossilized evidence of animal activity on or within soft sediment

3. the trace or remains of an organism that lived long ago

5. the impression left in sediment or rock where a plant or animal was buried

SECTION SUMMARY

Read the following section summary.

Fossils are the traces or remains of an organism that lived long ago.

Fossils can be preserved in sedimentary rock, amber, asphalt, or ice and by petrification.

Trace fossils are any naturally preserved evidence of animal activity. Tracks, burrows, and coprolites are examples of trace fossils.

Scientists study fossils to determine how environments and organisms have changed over time.

An index fossil is a fossil that can be used to establish the age of rock layers.

Skills Worksheet

Vocabulary and Section Summary B

Earth's Changing Continents
VOCABULARY

After you finish reading the section, try this puzzle! The underlined words and phrases below are missing all their vowels. Write the completed word or phrase in the space provided.

1. <u>CNTNNTL DRFT</u> describes how continents have moved around Earth's surface throughout Earth's history.

_____

2. Plate movements changed Earth's climate and affected <u>VLTN</u>, or how populations of species have changed over time.

_____

3. The theory that explains how Earth's tectonic plates move and change shape is called <u>PLT TCTNCS</u>.

_____

4. The thin, cool "skin" of Earth is called the <u>LTHSPHR</u>.

_____

5. Tectonic plates rest on a thick layer of solid rock called the <u>MNTL</u>.

_____

6. Plates move toward each other at a(n) <u>CNVRGNT BNDRY</u>.

_____

7. Plates moving apart at a(n) <u>DVRGNT BNDRY</u> form a giant crack in the lithosphere.

_____

8. The movement of the plates can cause earthquakes in the area of a(n) <u>TRNSFRM BNDRY</u>.

_____

Vocabulary and Section Summary B *continued*

SECTION SUMMARY

Read the following section summary.

Earth's tectonic plates drift over time, moving continents and changing oceans.

Evidence from rocks and fossils shows how Earth's continents have drifted and how climate and life have changed as a result.

The breakup of Pangaea about 245 million years ago divided Earth's land into separate continents.

The movement of continents alters climates by changing the patterns of air currents and ocean currents.

The formation of the Panama Land Bridge is an example of how the movement of tectonic plates affects the distribution of organisms on Earth.

Name _____ Class _____ Date _____

Vocabulary and Section Summary B

Time Marches On
VOCABULARY

After you finish the section, try this puzzle! Use the clues below to fill in the blanks. Then, unscramble the letters in the numbered blanks to answer the question on the next page.

1. the death of every member of a species

___ ___ ___ ___ ___ ___
20   4   6   28

2. the standard method used to divide Earth's long natural history into manageable parts

___ ___ ___ ___ ___ ___ ___ ___ ___ ___ ___ ___ ___ ___
   19   15   25

___ ___ ___ ___ ___
  1

3. what eras are divided into

___ ___ ___ ___ ___ ___ ___
   17 22

4. the largest divisions of geologic time

___ ___ ___ ___
 3 27

5. the second-largest divisions of geologic time

___ ___ ___ ___ ___
12 2

6. what periods are divided into

___ ___ ___ ___ ___ ___
 7   24   10

7. the process of organisms using sunlight to produce their own food

___ ___ ___ ___ ___ ___ ___ ___ ___ ___ ___ ___ ___ ___
   14   21   26

8. a layer of gas in the upper atmosphere that absorbs harmful radiation from the sun

___ ___ ___ ___ ___
 8   23

Vocabulary and Section Summary B *continued*

9. organisms that contain a nucleus and other structures in their cells

___ ___ ___ ___ ___ ___ ___ ___
   9   5   18

10. single-celled organisms that lack a nucleus

___ ___ ___ ___ ___ ___ ___ ___ ___ ___
         16   13   11

11. What event describes the extinction of all the dinosaurs and about half of the animal and plant species?

___ ___ ___ ___ ___ ___ ___ ___ ___ ___ ___
 1   2   3   4   5   6   7   8   9   10

___ ___ ___ ___ ___ ___ ___ ___
11 12 13 14 15 16 17 18

___ ___ ___ ___ ___ ___ ___ ___ ___ ___
19 20 21 22 23 24 25 26 27 28

SECTION SUMMARY

Read the following section summary.

The geologic time scale divides Earth's 4.6 billion-year history into time intervals. These intervals include eons, eras, periods, and epochs.

At certain times in Earth's history, the number of different kinds of organisms has increased or decreased dramatically.

Life on Earth developed more than 3.6 billion years ago, during Precambrian time. After cyanobacteria added oxygen to the atmosphere, more-complex forms of life evolved.

A variety of marine organisms appeared at the beginning of the Paleozoic Era in what is called the Cambrian explosion. Near the end of the Paleozoic Era, the Permian extinction resulted in the disappearance of many organisms from the fossil record.

Dinosaurs dominated Earth during the Mesozoic Era. They all became extinct during the Cretaceous-Tertiary extinction.

Mammals have dominated the Cenozoic Era. Modern humans appeared during this era.

Name _____ Class _____ Date _____

Directed Reading B

Section: Change over Time (pp. 298–305)

1. One way to tell kinds of animals apart is by their _____.

DIFFERENCES BETWEEN ORGANISMS

_____ **2.** How does adaptation help an organism?
   a. It helps the organism change colors.
   b. It improves its ability to survive and reproduce.
   c. It improves its ability to change species.
   d. It helps the organism become a fossil.

_____ **3.** If living things have the same characteristics, they may be members of the same
   a. evolution.   **c.** species.
   b. planet.   **d.** fossil record.

4. Two organisms that can mate to produce offspring that can reproduce

belong to the same _____.

5. When members of the same species live in the same place, they form

a(n) _____.

6. Since life began on Earth, many _____ have vanished and many new ones have appeared.

7. Scientists have observed that species have _____ over time.

8. The inherited _____ in populations also change over time.

9. What can result as populations of organisms change?

_____

10. The process in which populations change over time is called

_____.

EVIDENCE OF CHANGES OVER TIME

_____ **11.** Where is evidence that organisms have changed over time buried?
   a. within Earth's crust   **c.** in water
   b. on the Internet   **d.** in old books

_____ **12.** What is a fossil?
  a. a layer of sediment
  b. a living organism
  c. a very old organism
  d. the trace or remains of an organism that lived long ago

13. How is a fossil usually formed?

_____

_____

_____

_____

14. What is the timeline of life that scientists have made by studying fossils called?

_____

15. How are fossils organized in the fossil record?

_____

_____

16. Fossils in newer layers of Earth tend to resemble

current _____.

17. In older layers of Earth, are fossils more likely or less likely to resemble today's animals or plants?

_____

18. What does comparing organisms in the fossil record provide evidence for?

_____

_____

EVIDENCE OF ANCESTRY

_____ **19.** The fossil record provides evidence about
  a. the age of rocks.
  b. the order in which species have existed.
  c. the number of layers Earth has.
  d. the composition of minerals.

_____ **20.** In fossils and in living things, scientists find evidence of
        a. common ancestors.
        b. rock layers of Earth.
        c. the age of rocks.
        d. the composition of minerals.

21. As scientists study fossils and living organisms, they may draw models to

illustrate their _____ about how species are related.

22. What is the model that shows the relationship between species called?

_____

23. What does each branch in this model represent?

_____

24. List two groups of animals that may share a common ancestor with whales.

_____

_____

25. Scientists use information about organisms to sketch out

a(n)_____ that includes all known living things.

EXAMINING ORGANISMS

26. In addition to studying fossils, how can scientists learn about an organism's
ancestors?

_____

_____

27. List three things about whales that tell scientists that whales are not fish.

_____

_____

_____

28. What do these traits show about whales?

_____

29. What does a whale body contain that hints it had an ancestor that lived
on land?

_____

_____

COMPARING ORGANISMS

_____ **30.** Which of the following scientific fields provide evidence that organisms share common ancestors?
a. physical education and comparative molecules
b. geology and geography
c. comparative anatomy and molecular biology
d. physics and chemistry

_____ **31.** When scientists study the anatomy of organisms, they find that related organisms
a. share all their traits.
b. share many traits.
c. share no traits.
d. have no traits.

_____ **32.** Which of the following makes the human arm similar to a dolphin's flipper or a bat's wing?
a. the ability to fly
b. the structure of the skin
c. the order of their evolution
d. the structure and order of bones

_____ **33.** What does the similarity between humans, dolphins, cats, and bats indicate?
a. that they all evolved recently
b. that their ancestors lived in the same place
c. that they share a common ancestor
d. that they are becoming more alike over time

_____ **34.** Which of the following determines an organism's traits?
a. its descendants
b. genetic information stored in its DNA
c. where it was born
d. what it looks like

35. What does comparing DNA from two species tell scientists ?

_____

_____

_____

Skills Worksheet

Directed Reading B

Section: How Does Evolution Happen? (pp. 306–311)

1. List three things that scientists learned about Earth beginning in the 1800s.

_____

_____

_____

CHARLES DARWIN

_____ **2.** What did Darwin do in order to study plants and animals?
   a. He took a trip around the world.
   b. He studied theology.
   c. He formed theories.
   d. He became a doctor.

_____ **3.** What did Darwin do during his travels?
   a. He wrote a book about his theory.
   b. He observed plants and animals.
   c. He took photos of plants and animals.
   d. He visited all the continents.

4. Darwin noticed that the plants and animals on the _____

were similar to, but not the same as, those in Ecuador.

5. What was one way that finches on different islands differed from each other?

_____

6. What was the beak of each finch adapted to?

_____

DARWIN'S THINKING

_____ **7.** What puzzled Darwin about the Galápagos finches?
   a. They were so different.
   b. They should not have been there.
   c. They were too similar.
   d. They were similar but had unique adaptations.

_____ **8.** A characteristic that can be passed from parent to offspring through genes is a(n)
   a. species.   **c.** trait.
   b. breeding.   **d.** adaptation.

9. What hypothesis did Darwin develop about the Galápagos finches?

_____

_____

_____

_____

Match the correct description with the correct term. Write the letter in the space provided.

_____ **10.** the idea that human populations can grow faster than the food supply

_____ **11.** the idea that Earth had formed naturally over a long period of time

_____ **12.** the practice of breeding plants and animals to have desired traits

a. Lyell's theory

b. selective breeding

c. Malthus's principle

13. Why do farmers and breeders use selective breeding?

_____

_____

14. Why might selective breeding be used in horses?

_____

_____

15. Why might selective breeding be used in fruit trees?

_____

_____

16. After reading Malthus's theory, Darwin realized that any species can

produce many _____.

17. The populations of all species are limited by starvation, disease, predation,

or _____.

18. Darwin reasoned that survivors had traits that helped them

_____ in their environment.

Directed Reading B *continued*

19. Darwin believed that offspring of these survivors inherit

the _____ that help them survive.

20. What idea of Darwin's about species was supported by Charles Lyell's book?

_____

_____

DARWIN'S THEORY OF NATURAL SELECTION

21. What was the name of Darwin's famous book?

_____

22. What theory did Darwin introduce in the book?

_____

23. What is natural selection?

_____

_____

_____

_____

Match the correct description with the correct step in natural selection. Write the letter in the space provided.

_____ **24.** Many more offspring are produced than will survive.

_____ **25.** No two offspring are alike.

_____ **26.** Many offspring will be killed before reproducing.

_____ **27.** The best adapted organisms will have many offspring that survive.

a. inherited variation

b. struggle to survive

c. overproduction

d. successful reproduction

28. List two things that Darwin did not know in relation to his theory.

_____

_____

_____

144 The Evolution of Living Things

29. What do scientists today know about how variation happens?

_____

_____

_____

30. Some _____ make an organism more likely to survive to reproduce.

31. When organisms carry genes that make them more likely to survive to reproduce than organisms that do not carry these genes, the process called _____ occurs.

Skills Worksheet

Directed Reading B

Section: Natural Selection in Action (pp. 312–317)

_____ 1. Which of the following can the theory of evolution by natural selection explain about a population?
   a. how it could become separated
   b. how it can change in response to its environment
   c. what its DNA looks like
   d. where it lives

CHANGES IN POPULATIONS

_____ 2. Which of the following things determine which traits in a population are favorable and which are unfavorable?
   a. genetic differences
   b. separation factors
   c. environmental factors
   d. fossil records

_____ 3. Which of the following are responsible for the differences between species and for differences between individuals in the same population?
   a. fossil records
   b. scientific experiments
   c. genetic differences
   d. reproductive isolation

4. A measure of how much members of a population differ genetically is

   called _____.

5. Individuals in a population with high genetic variation have different forms

   of their genes called _____.

6. What will a population with different alleles have?

   _____

7. What are populations with low genetic variation less likely to do?

   _____

   _____

   _____

8. What are environmental factors?

_____

_____

_____

9. What are three types of environmental factors that might affect organisms?

_____

_____

_____

10. Why would a green snake be better able to survive and reproduce in an environment of tall green grass than a brown snake would?

_____

_____

_____

_____

FORMING A NEW SPECIES

Match the correct description with the correct term. Write the letter in the space provided.

_____ **11.** the formation of new species as a result of evolution

_____ **12.** changes in response to the environment

_____ **13.** the loss of ability of separated groups to interbreed

_____ **14.** the moving apart of groups in a population

a. adaptation

b. reproductive isolation

c. separation

d. speciation

15. When part of a population becomes separated from the rest,

_____ often begins.

16. Movements of Earth's continental and oceanic plates can affect

the _____ of organisms.

17. Through adaptation, members of separated groups may develop

different _____.

18. If environmental conditions differ, _____ will also differ.

Directed Reading B *continued*

19. When members of two separated groups of a population can no longer inter-

breed, the two groups are members of different _____.

EXTINCTION

_____ **20.** If the adaptations of a species in a changed environment are not
sufficient for organisms to survive, the species may become
a. stronger.
b. isolated.
c. extinct.
d. adapted.

_____ **21.** A species is extinct when
a. it competes with other species.
b. it changes in response to its environment.
c. only a few members survive.
d. it has died out completely.

22. List three examples of environmental factors that can lead to the extinction of
organisms.

_____

_____

_____

23. When food and water in an environment decrease, there is increased

_____ among species for these resources, which may

lead to extinction of the losers.

24. Sometimes humans introduce new _____ into an area,
and other species living there may not have adaptations to escape them.

25. When a population loses its _____, it may not be adapted
to live elsewhere and may go extinct.

Skills Worksheet

Vocabulary and Section Summary B

Change over Time
VOCABULARY

After you finish reading the section, try this puzzle! Use the clues below to solve the following crossword puzzle.

ACROSS

4. the history of life in the geologic past as indicated by the traces or remains of living things

5. the trace or remains of an organism that lived long ago, most commonly preserved in sedimentary rock

DOWN

1. the process in which inherited characteristics within a population change over generations such that new species sometimes arise

2. a group of organisms that are closely related and can mate to produce fertile offspring

3. a characteristic that improves an individual's ability to survive and reproduce in a particular environment

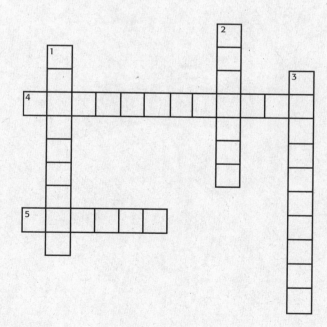

Vocabulary and Section Summary B *continued*

SECTION SUMMARY

Read the following section summary.

- Evolution is the process in which the inherited characteristics within a population change over generations, sometimes giving rise to new species.

- Fossils provide clues about the animals that have lived on Earth. Comparing fossils and living organisms supports the idea that organisms have changed over time.

- Scientists think that modern whales evolved from an ancient, land-dwelling mammal ancestor. Fossil organisms that support this hypothesis have been found.

- Comparing the anatomy and molecules of different organisms provides evidence of common ancestry among living organisms. The traits and DNA of species that have a common ancestor are more similar to each other than they are to the traits and DNA of distantly related species.

Skills Worksheet

Vocabulary and Section Summary B

How Does Evolution Happen?
VOCABULARY

After you finish reading the section, try this puzzle! In the space provided, write the term described. Then, find the words in the word search puzzle on the next page. Words are hidden vertically, horizontally, diagonally, and backward.

_____ **1.** a genetically determined characteristic

_____ **2.** the human practice of breeding animals or plants that have certain desired traits

_____ **3.** the process by which individuals that are better adapted to their environment survive and reproduce more successfully than less well-adapted individuals do; a theory to explain the mechanism of evolution

_____ **4.** a scientist who studies nature

_____ **5.** the process in which inherited characteristics within a population change over generations such that new species sometimes arise

Vocabulary and Section Summary B *continued*

W	T	M	S	F	N	W	S	S	P	T	V	J	I	I	I	S	C	V	Z
X	K	S	W	E	Z	O	K	T	I	E	T	T	C	E	E	Z	V	D	O
S	R	T	I	Z	F	G	W	A	C	O	K	B	V	L	X	H	D	S	I
Z	Y	V	O	L	C	J	R	H	E	J	M	K	E	G	V	C	V	P	N
J	U	B	O	D	A	T	O	R	D	O	I	C	P	X	S	N	B	R	O
M	B	P	J	H	N	R	S	W	N	W	T	U	F	B	W	D	N	E	I
T	A	Z	N	O	U	M	U	X	E	I	F	Y	X	J	W	F	K	E	T
H	D	O	O	F	D	N	D	T	V	N	I	M	G	X	A	S	W	H	U
V	B	R	T	Y	N	C	G	E	A	I	Z	G	R	V	R	V	E	W	L
I	I	M	G	B	R	C	B	O	A	N	J	K	T	F	P	N	D	C	O
P	K	N	T	P	G	R	R	M	G	Y	U	T	W	E	C	Z	X	C	V
O	X	I	T	M	E	V	T	Y	V	A	S	W	Y	H	D	A	I	B	E
G	E	F	J	E	A	V	R	X	V	M	Q	P	L	B	C	X	S	W	Z
E	Z	U	D	K	F	S	A	P	H	Y	B	H	Z	B	R	U	P	A	V
G	U	I	M	F	P	Z	Q	U	Y	B	L	V	U	O	V	W	A	Y	M
I	N	U	M	X	D	B	X	B	J	H	P	F	N	C	J	I	C	F	B
G	F	V	N	O	E	J	A	G	V	M	P	U	R	U	N	X	V	Z	I
K	C	N	O	I	T	C	E	L	E	S	L	A	R	U	T	A	N	J	I
F	S	A	S	L	P	X	U	I	L	E	I	L	K	N	R	I	A	I	P

SECTION SUMMARY

Read the following section summary.

- Finch species of the Galápagos Islands evolved adaptations in response to their environment.

- Natural selection is the process by which organisms that are better adapted to their environment are more likely to survive and reproduce than less well adapted organisms do.

- The four steps of Darwin's theory of evolution by natural selection include overproduction, inherited variation, struggle to survive, and successful reproduction.

- Variation in each species is due to the exchange of genetic information as it is passed from parent to offspring.

Skills Worksheet

Vocabulary and Section Summary B

Natural Selection in Action
VOCABULARY

After you finish reading the section, try this puzzle! Unscramble the letters at the end of each description to find the word that is being described. Arrange the boxed letters to make up a new word in the space provided.

1. forms of the genes of a population with high genetic variation: SLLLAEE

☐ _ _ _ _ _

2. condition where two separated groups become very different and are unable to interbreed when reunited: RPOVIERTUDEC LNIOAOSIT

_ _ _ _ _ ☐ _ _ _ _ _ _   _ _ _ _ ☐ _ _ _ _

3. the formation of new species as a result of evolution: PIOCNIETAS

_ ☐ _ _ _ _ ☐ _ _ _

4. a measure of how much individuals in a population differ genetically: TGENICE IAONAVRTI

_ _ _ _ ☐ _ _   _ _ _ _ ☐ _ _ _ _

5. the conditions in an environment that affect the organisms that live there: RINLMTAVEENON RAOTCFS

_ _ _ ☐ _ _ _ _ _ _ _ _ _   _ _ _ _ ☐ _ _ _

6. describes a species that has died out completely: CIENXTT

_ _ _ _ ☐ _ _

7. What is the new word?

_ _ _ _ _ _ _ _ _

Vocabulary and Section Summary B *continued*

SECTION SUMMARY

Read the following section summary.

- A population that has high genetic variation will have many individuals with different sets of traits.

- Environmental factors determine which traits are favorable and which traits are unfavorable.

- Natural selection explains how one species evolves into another.

- Separation, adaptation, and reproductive isolation can lead to speciation.

- If environmental conditions change, a species may not be able to survive and may go extinct.

- Environmental conditions that can lead to extinction of species include increased competition, new predators, and loss of habitat.

Skills Worksheet

Directed Reading B

Section: Sorting It All Out (pp. 332–337)

1. What is classification?

_____

_____

WHY CLASSIFY?

_____ **2.** Which of the following is NOT a question typically answered by classification?
   a. What are the defining characteristics of each species?
   b. What living organisms will eventually become extinct?
   c. When did the characteristics of an organism evolve?
   d. What are the relationships between various species?

_____ **3.** Classifying living things helps scientists
   a. make sense of useful animals only.
   b. make sense of living things in the world.
   c. make sense of geographic features.
   d. make sense of the useful plants only.

HOW DO SCIENTISTS CLASSIFY ORGANISMS?

_____ **4.** Taxonomy is the science of
   a. stuffing and mounting animals.
   b. describing, classifying, and naming organisms.
   c. naming and describing rocks.
   d. describing geographical features.

_____ **5.** The eight-level system of classification that is similar to the one that Carolus Linnaeus developed
   a. included only plants.
   b. is no longer used.
   c. is still used today.
   d. does not include plants.

_____ **6.** The more closely related living things are to each other, the more
   a. characteristics they share.
   b. food they share.
   c. space they share.
   d. water they will share.

_____ 7. Organisms are thought to be closely related when they have
      a. almost no characteristics in common.
      b. no characteristics in common.
      c. few characteristics in common.
      d. many characteristics in common.

_____ 8. Lions and house cats can both retract their claws, but brown bears and platypuses cannot. Which two are most clearly related?
      a. lions and house cats.
      b. lions and platypuses.
      c. house cats and platypuses.
      d. house cats and brown bears.

9. What Swedish botanist and physician created the first organized, modern taxonomy?

_____

10. How many levels of classification do scientists use today?

_____

11. Why are the platypus, brown bear, lion, and house cat thought to be related to each other?

_____

_____

_____

12. What characteristics do the bear, lion, and house cat have that the platypus does not have?

_____

_____

LEVELS OF CLASSIFICATION

_____ 13. All organisms are
      a. classified into one of three domains.
      b. classified into one of six phyla.
      c. either plants or animals.
      d. either living or nonliving things.

_____ 14. Each kingdom of organisms is first divided into several
      a. genera.
      b. classes.
      c. orders.
      d. phyla.

_____ **15.** The smallest, most specific classification level is
  a. phylum.
  b. species.
  c. class.
  d. order.

16. The plural form of the word *phylum* is _____.

17. The singular form of the word *genera* is _____.

18. In order from largest to smallest, what are the eight levels of classification?

_____

_____

_____

_____

_____

_____

_____

SCIENTIFIC NAMES

19. No matter how many common names an organism might have, it only has

one _____.

20. How was the naming of organisms different before Carolus Linnaeus, and how was the system difficult for scientists?

_____

_____

_____

21. Who simplified the naming of living things by giving each species a two-part scientific name?

_____

22. In the scientific name for the Asian elephant, *Elephas maximus*, the word

Elephas indicates the animal's _____.

23. All genus names begin with a(n) _____.

24. All specific names begin with a(n) _____.

25. Scientific names contain information about a(n) _____.

26. Scientific names are usually in one of these two languages,

_____ or _____.

27. In the scientific name *Tyrannosaurus rex*, *rex*, the Latin word for "king," is

the _____ name.

28. What abbreviation do scientists sometimes use when referring to
Tyrannosaurus rex?

_____

EXTINCT ORGANISMS AND LIVING ORGANISMS

29. What can scientists tell about an extinct organism in relation to a living
organism with which it has many derived characteristics in common?

_____

FOSSILS AND BRANCHING DIAGRAMS

30. When did the *Hypohippus* appear? Into what organism did it likely evolve?

_____

_____

Skills Worksheet

Directed Reading B

Section: Domains and Kingdoms (pp. 338–343)

1. Before the discovery of organisms like euglena, all organisms were

classified as either _____ or _____.

THREE DOMAINS

_____ 2. Which characteristic is NOT true for organisms of the genus *Euglena*?
a. single celled
b. live in salt water
c. live in pond water
d. make their own food

_____ 3. What level of classification did scientists create when they realized new kingdoms could not solve larger classification problems?
a. species
b. genus
c. families
d. domains

_____ 4. A green color and the ability to make food through photosynthesis might make some people think that members of the genus *Euglena* are
a. trees.
b. herbs.
c. plants.
d. mosses.

_____ 5. Which is a characteristic that animals and members of the genus *Euglena* possess but plants do not?
a. ability to move by themselves
b. ability to make food
c. ability to take in water
d. ability to use energy

6. Scientists added the kingdom _____, creating a

classification for organisms that were hard to classify as either fungi, plants, or animals.

7. Today, there are _____ domains in the classification

system.

Directed Reading B *continued*

DOMAIN ARCHAEA

8. Single-celled organisms that do not have a nucleus are called

_____.

DOMAIN BACTERIA

Identify the correct domains for the organisms described below by writing *Archaea* **or** *Bacteria* **in the space provided.**

_____ **9.** Some of these live inside humans.

_____ **10.** One of these causes pneumonia.

_____ **11.** These live in places where most other organisms could not live.

_____ **12.** Some of these can be found in hot springs in Yellowstone National Park.

_____ **13.** One type turns milk into yogurt.

DOMAIN EUKARYA

14. All organisms whose cells have a nucleus and membrane-bound organelles

are called _____.

15. All eukaryotes belong to the domain _____.

16. Members of the kingdom Protista are called _____.

17. Protists that have animal-like characteristics are called

_____.

18. Protists that have plantlike characteristics are called

_____.

19. Unlike plants, fungi do not use _____.

20. Unlike animals, _____ do not eat food.

21. How do fungi absorb nutrients from their surroundings?

_____

22. Give two examples of fungi.

_____

_____

23. What do all members of the kingdom Plantae have in common?

_____

_____

_____

24. In order for most plants to make their own food through photosynthesis,

they must be exposed to _____.

25. Plants can be found growing on _____ and in

_____ that light can penetrate.

26. Explain why the food that plants make is important not only to the plants
themselves but to other organisms as well.

_____

_____

_____

27. Besides making food that can be used by other organisms, plants also provide
nutrients. What is another way that trees and flowering plants are used by
animals?

_____

_____

_____

28. What characteristics do most members of kingdom Animalia share?

_____

_____

29. Members of kingdom Animalia have specialized sense organs that allow

them to respond to their _____.

30. Members of kingdom Animalia are commonly called

_____.

31. Explain why animals need plants.

_____

_____

32. Explain how animals depend on bacteria and fungi.

_____

_____

STRANGE ORGANISMS

33. The kingdom Animalia includes some very simple animals, such as

_____, that do not have sense organs and cannot move.

Name _____ Class _____ Date _____

Vocabulary and Section Summary B

Sorting It All Out
VOCABULARY

After you finish reading the section, try this puzzle! Use the clues given to fill in the blanks below. Then, copy the numbered letters into the corresponding boxes to reveal the levels of classification.

1. the science of describing, classifying, and naming organisms

__ __ __ __ __ __ __ __
       7   2

2. classifying organisms by their characteristics

__ __ __ __ __ __ __ __ __ __ __ __
       4   10

3. putting things in orderly groups based on their characteristics

__ __ __ __ __ __ __ __ __ __ __ __ __
 3   11   13

4. shows which characteristics organisms share and when they evolved

__ __ __ __ __ __ __ __ __ __
 14   1   15   5

5. characteristics that two or more kinds of organisms share with their most recent common ancestor

__ __ __ __ __ __ __ __ __ __
    6   12

__ __ __ __ __ __ __ __ __ __
 9   8

Vocabulary and Section Summary B *continued*

Organize the levels of classification from most to least general below.

a. _____

b. _____

c. _____

d. _____

e. _____

f. _____

g. _____

h. _____

SECTION SUMMARY

Read the following section summary.

- Classification groups organisms based on their shared derived characteristics.
- Classification is a tool that helps us understand the relationships between organisms.
- There are eight levels of classification.
- The scientific name of an organism has two parts.
- Branching diagrams show evolutionary relationships between extinct and living organisms.

Skills Worksheet

Vocabulary and Section Summary B

Domains and Kingdoms
VOCABULARY

After you finish reading the section, try this puzzle! In the space provided, write the term described. Then, find those words in the word search puzzle on the next page. Terms can be hidden in the puzzle vertically, horizontally, diagonally, or backward.

For each of the following descriptions, write the kingdom or domain of the organisms being described.

_____ **1.** single-celled organisms without nuclei, such as *Escherichia coli*, which live in the human body

_____ **2.** multicellular, eukaryotic organisms that are usually green and make sugar through photosynthesis

_____ **3.** prokaryotes that were first discovered living in extreme environments where other organisms could not survive

_____ **4.** multicellular organisms whose cells have nuclei but do not have cell walls

_____ **5.** multicellular organisms that have cells containing nuclei and that absorb nutrients from their surroundings after breaking them down with digestive juices

_____ **6.** single-celled or simple multicellular eukaryotic organisms

_____ **7.** organisms whose cells have a nucleus and membrane-bound organelles

Vocabulary and Section Summary B *continued*

D	I	C	H	O	T	A	Y	R	A	K	U	E	Y	I
Y	A	L	S	Y	A	R	Z	A	U	R	Q	W	F	J
G	F	A	S	P	X	E	S	K	P	P	X	B	I	U
P	K	S	O	H	O	X	A	N	S	S	K	A	F	Y
E	E	S	F	U	N	G	I	I	N	W	I	C	A	Y
C	G	I	Y	G	O	F	T	P	L	A	N	T	A	E
P	D	F	H	X	M	K	F	L	K	A	S	E	C	Q
W	M	I	G	H	Y	N	F	O	Z	I	M	R	F	P
A	R	C	H	A	E	A	A	C	T	E	R	I	A	M
P	G	A	R	L	R	W	S	O	F	S	R	A	N	I
V	U	T	J	X	I	F	R	L	B	V	N	Y	F	A
J	W	I	S	T	W	P	U	O	A	F	N	L	F	D
D	S	O	Y	G	E	O	I	X	Y	R	A	C	K	K
S	F	N	E	K	D	W	D	X	Q	H	Z	T	S	C

SECTION SUMMARY

Read the following section summary.

- Most biologists recognize three domains: Archaea, Bacteria, and Eukarya.

- As scientists discover new organisms, classification systems are changed to include the characteristics of those new organisms.

- Archaea can live in extreme environments. Bacteria live almost everywhere else. All prokaryotes are members of the domain Archaea or the domain Bacteria.

- Domain Eukarya is made up of four kingdoms: Protista, Fungi, Plantae, and Animalia. All members of Eukarya are eukaryotes.

Skills Worksheet

Directed Reading B

Section: What Is a Plant? (pp. 360–363)

1. Why couldn't you eat much without plants?

_____

_____

_____

PLANT CHARACTERISTICS

_____ 2. What does the cuticle do?
   a. It captures energy from the sun.
   b. It creates air.
   c. It keeps plants from drying out.
   d. It grows into chloroplasts.

_____ 3. What is the name of the green pigment that captures energy from the sun?
   a. organelles
   b. chlorophyll
   c. carbon dioxide
   d. chloroplasts

_____ 4. Plants use energy from sunlight to make food from carbon dioxide and water in a process called
   a. chloroplasts.
   b. organelles.
   c. photosynthesis.
   d. producers.

Match the correct definition with the correct term. Write the letter in the space provided.

_____ 5. rigid structure that surrounds a plant cell

_____ 6. structure that contains chlorophyll

_____ 7. structure that stores water

_____ 8. one substance that forms a hard material in cell walls

_____ 9. structure that lies beneath the cell wall

a. vacuole
b. cell membrane
c. cell wall
d. carbohydrates
e. chloroplast

10. Plants have two stages in their _____.

11. Plants make spores in the _____ stage.

Directed Reading B *continued*

12. When the spores of some plants grow, the new plants are

called _____.

13. These new plants then produce eggs and _____.

14. The fertilized egg of a gametophyte grows into a(n) _____.

PLANT CLASSIFICATION

Match the correct description with the correct term. Write the letter in the space provided.

_____ **15.** an example of a nonvascular plant

_____ **16.** plants without specialized conducting tissues

_____ **17.** an example of a seedless vascular plant

_____ **18.** plants that have tissues to deliver water and nutrients from one part of the plant to another

_____ **19.** vascular seed plant that does not flower

_____ **20.** flowering plant with seeds

a. nonvascular plants

b. vascular plants

c. gymnosperm

d. angiosperm

e. fern

f. liverwort

THE ORIGIN OF PLANTS

21. Although some algae are green, they are not _____.

22. What are five similarities between modern green algae and plants?

_____

_____

_____

_____

23. Because of their similarities, some scientists think modern green algae

and plants share a common _____.

Directed Reading B

Section: Seedless Plants (pp. 364–367)

1. List the two groups of seedless plants.

_____

_____

NONVASCULAR PLANTS

_____ **2.** Nonvascular plants get the water they need
   a. from rhizomes.
   b. from the environment or nearby cells.
   c. from the ground through their roots.
   d. from vascular tissues.

_____ **3.** Rhizoids are like roots because
   a. they contain vascular tissue.
   b. they do not contain vascular tissue.
   c. they help hold the plant in place.
   d. they live in large groups.

_____ **4.** Rhizoids help nonvascular plants
   a. become tall and leafy.
   b. develop vascular parts.
   c. obtain water and nutrients.
   d. produce spores.

_____ **5.** Which of the following is true of liverworts?
   a. They usually live in dry places.
   b. They are very large.
   c. They are vascular plants.
   d. Their gametophytes can be mosslike and leafy.

6. List three reasons why nonvascular plants are important.

_____

_____

_____

SEEDLESS VASCULAR PLANTS

7. Seedless vascular plants are often larger than _____
   plants.

8. What is vascular tissue specialized to do?

_____

9. An underground stem from which new leaves and roots grow is called

a(n) _____.

10. Young fronds are called _____ because of how they are coiled.

11. Describe the fern gametophyte.

_____

_____

_____

12. Ferns rely on _____ for sexual reproduction.

13. Ferns and other seedless vascular plants reproduce sexually

and _____.

Match the correct description with the correct term. Write the letter in the space provided.

_____ **14.** structure where silica is found in horsetails

_____ **15.** substance that has a gritty texture

_____ **16.** plants that have life cycles similar to horsetails and club mosses

_____ **17.** used by pioneers to scrub pans

_____ **18.** plants that grow in woodlands

_____ **19.** tissue found in club mosses but not in mosses

a. club mosses
b. stem
c. horsetails
d. vascular tissue
e. silica
f. ferns

20. What are four roles seedless vascular plants play in the environment?

_____

_____

_____

_____

Directed Reading B *continued*

21. Name two kinds of seedless vascular plants that are popular houseplants.

_____

_____

22. Name two kinds of seedless vascular plants that can be eaten by humans.

_____

_____

23. In what way are fossilized seedless vascular plants that died 300 million years ago important to humans?

_____

_____

_____

_____

Skills Worksheet

Directed Reading B

Section: Seed Plants (pp. 368–373)

1. How are gymnosperms and angiosperms different?

_____

_____

_____

CHARACTERISTICS OF SEED PLANTS

Fill in each blank with either "seedless plants" or "seed plants."

2. In _____, the gametophytes do not live independently of the sporophytes.

3. The gametophytes of _____ form within the reproductive structures of the sporophyte.

4. The sperm of _____ need water to swim to the eggs of female gametophytes.

5. The sperm of _____ can reach the eggs without the help of water.

6. The sperm of _____ form inside of pollen, which is carried by wind or by animals.

7. The most common plants on Earth are _____.

THE STRUCTURE OF SEEDS

Match the correct description with the correct term. Write the letter in the space provided.

_____ **8.** the young plant within a seed

_____ **9.** structure that surrounds and protects the young plant

_____ **10.** seed leaves of a young plant

_____ **11.** joining of sperm and egg

_____ **12.** often the purpose of the cotyledons

a. cotyledons

b. fertilization

c. food storage

d. seed coat

e. sporophyte

13. Name two advantages seeds have over spores.

_____

_____

GYMNOSPERMS

_____ **14.** Seed plants that do not have flowers or fruit are called
  a. sporophytes.   **c.** gametophytes.
  b. angiosperms.   **d.** gymnosperms.

_____ **15.** Gymnosperm seeds are usually protected by
  a. leaves.   **c.** fruits.
  b. cones.   **d.** humans.

_____ **16.** The most economically important gymnosperms are the
  a. conifers.   **c.** cycads.
  b. ginkgoes.   **d.** gnetophytes.

_____ **17.** Three things that conifers are used for are
  a. building materials, cancer drugs, and gardens and parks.
  b. paper products, resin, and syrup.
  c. allergy drugs, leather, and resin.
  d. building materials, fresh fruit, and gardens and parks.

Match the correct description with the correct term. Write the letter in the space provided.

_____ **18.** most are evergreens   **a.** ginkgoes

_____ **19.** group of gymnosperms that are shrubs that   **b.** cycads
         grow in dry areas
                                                            c. conifers

_____ **20.** group of gymnosperms with only one living   **d.** gnetophytes
         species

_____ **21.** gymnosperms that grow in the Tropics

22. During the pine tree's life cycle, sex cells are produced in the

_____ .

23. The male _____ of gymnosperms are found in pollen.

24. Pollen is carried from the male cone to the female cone

by _____.

25. Some cones release seeds only during _____.

26. The transfer of pollen from the male reproductive structures to the female

reproductive structures of seed plants is called _____.

ANGIOSPERMS

_____ **27.** About how many species of angiosperms can be found today?
   a. over 1,000   **c.** just a few
   b. at least 235,000   **d.** over one million

28. How are angiosperm fruits and seeds transported to new areas?

_____

_____

Each of the following phrases describes, or is an example of, either a monocot or a eudicot. In the space provided, write *M* for a monocot and *E* for a eudicot.

_____ **29.** plant that has one cotyledon (seed leaf)

_____ **30.** vascular tissue in bundles that are scattered

_____ **31.** plant that has two cotyledons

_____ **32.** flower parts in threes

_____ **33.** vascular tissue in a ring

_____ **34.** flower parts in fours or fives

35. Explain the difference between the way that a field mouse and the way that an owl obtain food from flowering plants.

_____

_____

_____

36. List three ways that people use flowering plants.

_____

_____

_____

Skills Worksheet)

Directed Reading B

Section: Structures of Seed Plants (pp. 374–381)

_____ 1. Vascular tissue that transports water and minerals through a plant is called
    a. shoots.   **c.** phloem.
    b. xylem.   **d.** leaves.

_____ 2. Vascular tissue that transports food molecules to all parts of a plant is called
    a. shoots.   **c.** phloem.
    b. xylem.   **d.** leaves.

ROOTS

3. Most root systems are located _____.

4. What are the three main functions of roots?

_____

_____

_____

Match the correct description with the correct term. Write the letter in the space provided.

_____ 5. cells of the epidermis that extend from the root

_____ 6. group of cells that produces a slimy substance

_____ 7. root system with one main root

_____ 8. layer of cells that covers root surfaces

_____ 9. plants that usually have fibrous roots

_____ 10. structure protected by the root cap

_____ 11. what root hairs increase

_____ 12. root system in which roots are usually the same size

a. fibrous root
b. root tip
c. epidermis
d. surface area
e. taproot
f. root hairs
g. monocots
h. root cap

STEMS

_____ **13.** Which of the following is NOT true about stems?
    a. Stems are always located above the ground.
    b. Stems connect the roots to the leaves and flowers.
    c. Stems hold up flowers so pollinators can see them.
    d. Stems can store water.

_____ **14.** What does xylem do?
    a. It carries food to plant parts.
    b. It dissolves minerals and food.
    c. It carries water and minerals from the roots to the leaves.
    d. It grows longer roots.

_____ **15.** What does phloem do?
    a. It carries food to plant parts.
    b. It participates in photosynthesis.
    c. It takes water and minerals to stems.
    d. It dissolves minerals.

_____ **16.** Stems that are soft, thin, and flexible are
    a. xylem.   **c.** phloem.
    b. herbaceous.   **d.** woody.

17. Name two examples of plants with herbaceous stems.

_____

_____

_____

18. What is a growth ring?

_____

_____

_____

_____

LEAVES

_____ **19.** What is the main function of leaves?
    a. They create water for the plant.
    b. They keep insects away from the plant.
    c. They make food for the plant.
    d. They absorb oxygen for the plant.

20. List the four layers in a leaf in order, from top to bottom.

_____

_____

_____

_____

21. Most photosynthesis takes place in the _____ in the
middle of the leaf.

Match the correct definition with the correct term. Write the letter in the space provided.

_____ **22.** cells that open and close the stomata

_____ **23.** layer of cells that contains many
chloroplasts

_____ **24.** a single layer of cells beneath the cuticle

_____ **25.** a tiny opening that allows carbon dioxide
to enter the leaf

_____ **26.** layer where carbon dioxide moves freely
and xylem and phloem are found

_____ **27.** structure that prevents water loss from
the leaf

a. stoma

b. guard cells

c. spongy layer

d. epidermis

e. palisade layer

f. cuticle

28. Cactus spines are _____ that are modified to protect
cactuses from animals.

29. The leaves of the sundew plant catch _____, which are
digested to provide nitrogen to the plant.

LOWERS

30. Why do some plants have flowers?

_____

_____

_____

31. In a flower, modified leaves called _____ protect the bud.

32. The broad, flat, thin leaflike parts of a flower, called

_____, attract insects and other animals.

33. The male reproductive structure of flowers is a(n) _____.

34. In flowers, a(n) _____ is the female reproductive
structure.

35. If the egg is fertilized, the _____ develops into a fruit and

the _____ develops into a seed.

36. List three ways that humans use flowers.

_____

_____

_____

Match the labels to the diagram. Write the letters in the spaces provided.

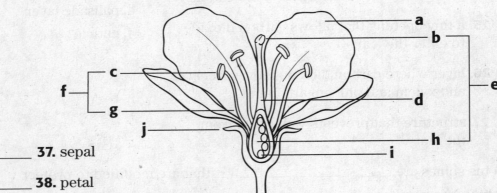

_____ **37.** sepal

_____ **38.** petal

_____ **39.** ovary

_____ **40.** ovule

_____ **41.** anther

_____ **42.** pistil

_____ **43.** filament

_____ **44.** stigma

_____ **45.** style

_____ **46.** stamen

Skills Worksheet

Vocabulary and Section Summary B

What Is a Plant?
VOCABULARY

After you finish reading the section, try this puzzle! Use the clues below to fill in the following crossword puzzle.

ACROSS

2. a process in which chloroplasts capture energy from sunlight to make food from carbon dioxide and water

5. a flowering plant that produces seeds within a fruit

DOWN

1. describes a plant that has specialized tissues that conduct materials from one part of the plant to another

3. a woody, vascular seed plant whose seeds are not enclosed by an ovary or fruit

4. describes a plant that lacks specialized conducting tissues and true roots, stems, and leaves

SECTION SUMMARY

Read the following section summary.

- All plants make their own food and have cuticles, cells walls, and a two-stage life cycle.

- Plants are first classified into two groups: nonvascular plants and vascular plants. Vascular plants are further divided into seedless plants, gymnosperms, and angiosperms.

- Similarities between green algae and plants suggest that they have a common ancestor.

Skills Worksheet

Vocabulary and Section Summary B

Seedless Plants

VOCABULARY

After you finish reading the section, try this puzzle! In the space provided, write the term described. Then, find the words in the puzzle on the next page. Words are hidden vertically, horizontally, diagonally, and backward.

Clues

_____ 1. a rootlike structure in nonvascular plants that holds the plants in place and helps plants get water and nutrients

_____ 2. a horizontal, underground stem that produces new leaves, shoots, and roots

_____ 3. tightly coiled fern leaves or fronds

_____ 4. a plant that lacks specialized conducting tissues and true roots, stems, and leaves

_____ 5. a plant that has specialized tissues that conduct materials from one part of the plant to another

Q	Z	W	S	D	P	C	Z	Q	N	F	D	V	S	Q	Y	E	L	L	Z
V	F	B	J	H	I	K	O	B	E	S	A	J	W	H	B	Q	E	C	O
O	R	L	J	V	B	F	N	F	S	S	E	Y	N	P	M	O	J	E	U
S	Z	M	R	Y	Q	P	I	E	C	U	N	W	K	O	W	Z	J	E	X
O	V	K	S	Z	H	Y	F	U	G	F	O	Z	A	M	A	M	E	E	Y
K	D	E	D	F	L	B	L	L	T	S	N	X	C	J	Q	H	V	U	R
F	V	O	G	G	X	A	K	U	N	S	V	H	J	J	P	I	L	A	J
D	W	K	M	M	R	F	L	I	B	E	A	P	C	P	L	J	J	E	Q
K	P	S	Q	P	E	R	E	A	B	G	S	O	A	H	R	D	E	J	X
E	A	J	L	R	M	R	G	P	L	I	C	T	C	T	K	Q	J	C	N
Y	Q	A	Y	G	O	C	E	H	K	I	U	U	Y	K	V	B	A	Q	B
Y	N	W	W	F	Z	F	D	C	V	O	L	Y	P	V	L	S	Z	R	W
T	U	A	W	Q	I	R	D	P	M	E	A	O	S	E	E	Z	W	H	B
J	R	C	C	Z	H	S	J	G	X	E	R	D	R	P	I	R	F	K	D
X	V	T	N	P	R	N	S	Y	P	T	P	L	I	L	G	P	V	Y	C
M	F	Z	R	T	J	T	V	E	V	G	L	V	U	O	J	T	H	Y	U
L	W	P	W	K	N	Z	S	Y	W	L	A	G	V	T	Z	J	A	E	F
S	A	H	Q	K	G	X	C	H	A	R	N	A	D	T	U	I	B	B	A
A	H	Y	Y	W	M	L	J	Z	X	Y	T	A	B	B	W	G	H	L	X
S	D	A	E	H	E	L	D	D	I	F	L	K	R	H	H	I	U	R	L

SECTION SUMMARY

Read the following section summary.

- Nonvascular plants include mosses, liverworts, and hornworts.
- Seedless vascular plants include ferns, horsetails, and club mosses.
- Most plants have a two-stage life cycle and reproduce both sexually and asexually.
- The rhizoids and rhizomes of seedless plants prevent erosion by holding soil in place. The remains of seedless vascular plants that lived and died about 300 million years ago formed coal.

Skills Worksheet

Vocabulary and Section Summary B

Seed Plants
VOCABULARY

After you finish reading the section, try this puzzle! In each of the following items, use the clue to unscramble the letters and write the term in the spaces below.

1. the tiny granules that contain the male gametophytes of seed plants: OPLNEL

_____

2. a type of gymnosperm that has male and female cones containing spores: NFERCOI

_____

3. the transfer of pollen from the male reproductive structures to the female structures of seed plants: TIPIOLNOALN

_____

4. a flowering plant that produces seeds within a fruit: GENAMIRSOP

_____

5. a woody, vascular seed plant whose seeds are not enclosed by an ovary or fruit: MEYRMNSGOP

_____

SECTION SUMMARY

Read the following section summary.

Seeds nourish the young sporophyte of seed plants. Seed plant gametophytes rely on the sporophyte. Also, they do not need water for fertilization.

Sexual reproduction occurs in gymnosperms when sperm from the male cone fertilizes the eggs of the female cone. The embryo develops within the female cone, which then releases seeds.

Flowers are the reproductive structures of angiosperms. Wind and animals help angiosperms reproduce.

Many organisms rely on seed plants for food. Humans have many uses for seed plants.

Skills Worksheet

Vocabulary and Section Summary B

Structures of Seed Plants

VOCABULARY

After you finish reading the section, try this puzzle! The underlined words below are missing all of their vowels. Look at each clue below, and use the clue to supply the vowels and unscramble the letters. Then, write the word in the blanks provided. The boxed letters will spell out a new phrase. Write the phrase at the bottom of the page.

1. In the ovary of a seed plant, the <u>LV</u> contains an embryo sac and develops into a seed after fertilization.

_ _ _ □ _

2. <u>MPHL</u> is tissue that conducts food in vascular plants.

_ _ _ □ _ _

3. The type of tissue in vascular plants that provides support and conducts water and nutrients from the roots is the <u>XLM</u>.

_ _ _ □ _

4. The <u>VR</u> in flowering plants is the lower part of a pistil that produces eggs in ovules.

_ _ _ □ _

5. In a flower, one of the outermost rings of modified leaves that protect the flower bud is called a <u>LPS</u>.

□ _ _ _ _

6. A <u>TPL</u> is one of the usually brightly colored leaf-shaped parts that make up one of the rings of a flower.

_ □ _ _ _

7. The male reproductive structure of a flower, or <u>TMSN</u>, produces pollen and consists of an anther at the tip of a filament.

_ _ _ _ □ _

8. The <u>TPLS</u> is the female reproductive part of a flower, which produces seeds and consists of an ovary, style, and stigma.

_ _ □ _ _ _

9. What is the phrase?

F _ _ **W** _ _ _   _ _ _ **D** _

SECTION SUMMARY

Read the following section summary.

Roots supply plants with water and dissolved minerals. Roots support and anchor plants. Roots also store surplus food made during photosynthesis.

Stems support the body of a plant. They allow transport of materials between the roots and shoots. Some stems store materials, such as water.

A leaf has a thin epidermis on its upper and lower surfaces. The epidermis allows sunlight to pass through to the center of the leaf.

Most photosynthesis takes place in the palisade layer of a leaf. The spongy layer of a leaf allows the movement of carbon dioxide and contains the xylem and phloem.

Flowers are the reproductive structures of angiosperms. They may have four parts: sepals, petals, stamens, and one or more pistils.

The pistil is usually located in the center of the flower. The ovary of a pistil contains ovules, which contain eggs. When the eggs are fertilized, ovules develop into seeds and the ovary becomes a fruit.

Skills Worksheet

Directed Reading B

Section: Photosynthesis (pp. 396–399)

_____ 1. In addition to oxygen, which of the following gases is important to plants?
 a. ozone   **c.** carbon dioxide
 b. methane   **d.** helium

2. Define *photosynthesis*.

_____

_____

3. Plants make a sugar called _____ from carbon dioxide and water.

CAPTURING LIGHT ENERGY

_____ 4. Which of the following capture sunlight energy for photosynthesis?
 a. water molecules
 b. roots
 c. glucose molecules
 d. chloroplasts

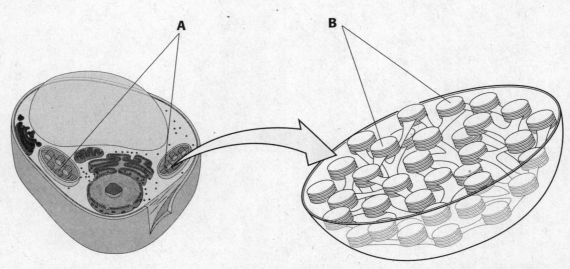

A   B

Match the label to the part of the drawing. Write the letter in the space provided.

_____ **5.** grana

_____ **6.** chloroplasts

7. The pigment in plants that absorbs light energy is called

_____.

8. The presence of what two things makes parts of a plant look green?

_____

_____

MAKING SUGAR

9. What is glucose, and what do plants use it for?

_____

_____

10. When photosynthesis takes place, plant cells give off

_____ gas.

GETTING ENERGY FROM SUGAR

_____ **11.** Which of the following release energy that is stored in glucose?
  a. sucrose molecules   **c.** mitochondria
  b. chloroplasts   **d.** grana

12. Define *cellular respiration*.

_____

_____

13. During cellular respiration, excess glucose is converted to another type

of sugar called _____ or stored as starch.

GAS EXCHANGE

Match the correct description with the correct term. Write the letter in the space provided.

_____ **14.** a waxy coating that protects the plant from
           water loss

_____ **15.** an opening in a plant leaf or stem that allows
           gas exchange to occur

_____ **16.** "double doors" that open and close the stoma

_____ **17.** the process by which plants lose water through
           their leaves

a. stoma

b. transpiration

c. cuticle

d. guard cells

Name _____ Class _____ Date _____

Directed Reading B *continued*

THE IMPORTANCE OF PHOTOSYNTHESIS

_____ **18.** Which of the following are photosynthetic organisms that can be found at the base of nearly all food chains on Earth?
   a. reptiles
   b. fish
   c. bacteria
   d. mammals

19. What process do plants, animals, and most other organisms rely on to get energy?

_____

_____

20. What product of photosynthesis do animals and plants need for cellular respiration?

_____

_____

Skills Worksheet

Directed Reading B

Section: Reproduction of Flowering Plants (pp. 400–403)

_____ 1. The largest and most diverse group of plants is made up of
  a. prairie grasses.
  b. trees.
  c. flowering plants.
  d. shrubs.

FERTILIZATION

Match the label to the parts of the drawing. Write the letter in the space provided. Some labels may be used more than once.

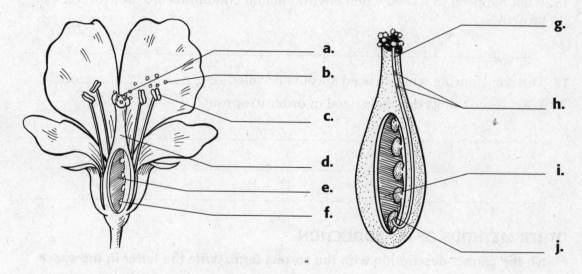

_____ 2. anther

_____ 3. ovary

_____ 4. ovule

_____ 5. ovule containing egg

_____ 6. pollen

_____ 7. pollen tube

_____ 8. sperm

_____ 9. stigma

_____ 10. style

Directed Reading B *continued*

11. When pollen is moved from anthers to stigmas, _____ takes place.

12. When sperm fuses with the egg inside an ovule, _____ takes place.

FROM FLOWER TO FRUIT

13. After fertilization takes place, the _____ develops into a seed.

14. After fertilization takes place, the _____ becomes a fruit.

FROM SEED TO PLANT

15. What happens to a seed when environmental conditions are unfavorable to growth?

_____

16. The stage during which a seed sprouts is called _____.

17. What three things do seeds need in order to sprout?

_____

_____

_____

OTHER METHODS OF REPRODUCTION

Match the correct description with the correct term. Write the letter in the space provided.

_____ **18.** above-ground stems from which new plants can grow

_____ **19.** tiny plants that grow along the edges of a plant's leaves, fall off, and grow on their own

_____ **20.** underground stems from which new plants can grow

a. plantlets

b. tubers

c. runners

Skills Worksheet

Directed Reading B

Section: Plant Development and Responses (pp. 404–409)

_____ 1. The process that an organism goes through as it increases in ability or skill is called
   a. development.   **c.** growth.
   b. pollination.   **d.** dormancy.

_____ 2. Growth refers to
   a. a decrease in size.
   b. an increase in size.
   c. a change in color.
   d. a decrease in chlorophyll.

_____ 3. When a cell is specialized to perform a specific function, it has become
   a. fertilized.   **c.** differentiated.
   b. pollinated.   **d.** dormant.

PLANT DEVELOPMENT

4. In what way do some plant cells differ from animal cells?

_____

_____

Match the correct description with the correct term. Write the letter in the space provided.

_____ 5. anything that causes a reaction or change in an organism   **a.** hormone

b. stimulus

_____ 6. a chemical that causes some plant cells to differentiate in response to stimuli

PLANT HORMONES

7. Name three environmental stimuli that affect the amount of a particular hormone that is made in plant cells.

_____

_____

8. Plant hormones called _____ cause plants to grow toward light.

9. Name two hormones that are useful in agriculture.

_____

_____

PLANT TROPISMS

10. Define *tropism*.

_____

11. A change in the direction of plant growth that is caused by light is

called _____.

12. Plant growth that changes in response to the direction of gravity is

called _____.

Match the correct description with the correct term. Write the letter in the space provided.

_____ **13.** plant growth toward a stimulus

_____ **14.** plant growth away from a stimulus

a. positive tropism

b. negative tropism

In the spaces below, write the letter _P_ if the example has positive gravitropism or the letter _N_ if it has negative gravitropism.

_____ **15.** shoot tips

_____ **16.** root tips

17. Gravitropism is also known as _____.

SEASONAL RESPONSES

18. What would happen if a plant bloomed during a cold winter?

_____

_____

19. Why are plants that live in areas with cold winters able to detect the change in seasons?

_____

_____

_____

20. Plants that flower when nights are long are called _____.

21. Plants that flower when nights are short are called _____.

22. Why is the difference between the length of day and length of night an important environmental stimulus for plants?

_____

_____

23. Why do the leaves of some deciduous trees change color in the fall?

_____

_____

_____

_____

In the spaces below, write the letter "D" if the tree is deciduous or "E" if it is an evergreen.

_____ **24.** maple

_____ **25.** oak

_____ **26.** pine

_____ **27.** elm

Match the correct description with the correct term. Write the letter in the space provided.

_____ **28.** trees that lose all of their leaves around the same time each year

_____ **29.** trees that shed some of their leaves year-round

a. evergreen tree

b. deciduous tree

Skills Worksheet

Vocabulary and Section Summary B

Photosynthesis

VOCABULARY

After you finish reading the section, try this puzzle! Use the clues to unscramble each of the words below, and write the word in the space provided.

1. the opening in a leaf's surface that allows gases to pass through: OTSMA

_ _ _ _ ☐

2. green pigment that captures light energy: PROLYCHHOLL

_ ☐ _ ☐ _ _ _ _ _ _

3. process by which plants make their own food: SISOTOPHSENYHT

☐ _ ☐ _ _ _ _ _ _ _ _ _ _ _

4. process by which plants release energy from food: EUALCRLL
EAPRRIINOST (two words)

☐ _ ☐ _ _ ☐ _ _   _ _ ☐ _ _ _ _ _ _ _

5. the loss of water from leaves: AAIINNTTRRSPO

_ ☐ _ _ _ _ _ _ ☐ _ _ _

Now unscramble the boxed letters to find the organelle that contains the photosynthetic pigment in plants.

☐☐☐☐☐☐☐☐☐☐☐☐

SECTION SUMMARY

Read the following section summary.

• Chloroplasts and mitochondria are important organelles in plant cells.
• During photosynthesis, plants use energy from sunlight, carbon dioxide, and water to make glucose and oxygen.
• Plants get energy from food by cellular respiration, which uses oxygen and releases carbon dioxide and water.
• Transpiration, or the loss of water through the leaves of plants, occurs when stomata are open.

Skills Worksheet

Vocabulary and Section Summary B

Reproduction of Flowering Plants
VOCABULARY

After you finish reading the section, try this puzzle! Use the clues below to write the term described. Then, find those words in the puzzle below. Terms can be hidden in the puzzle vertically, horizontally, diagonally, or backward.

_____ 1. process that occurs when pollen is moved from anthers to stigma

_____ 2. a tiny, undeveloped plant inside of a seed

_____ 3. term that describes the inactive state of a seed or other plant part when conditions are unfavorable to growth

_____ 4. above-ground stem from which a new plant can grow

_____ 5. the sprouting of a seed

Q	D	G	L	P	A	B	R	X	Q	C	F	Q	W
P	R	U	N	N	E	R	M	J	K	N	O	Y	R
P	L	Y	I	P	R	M	P	I	A	G	T	F	O
O	D	C	M	F	M	O	B	L	E	R	W	L	T
L	B	W	H	I	L	H	Z	R	P	A	Z	C	W
L	X	X	I	U	X	Y	M	X	Y	H	D	M	E
I	F	W	B	E	N	I	P	O	U	O	A	F	W
N	K	H	J	L	N	K	W	Q	R	O	O	G	T
A	H	H	F	A	R	X	X	M	B	D	S	R	R
T	U	L	T	D	E	L	A	T	E	Z	L	T	K
I	T	I	E	R	G	N	W	K	B	U	M	Q	T
O	O	X	C	K	T	F	Y	B	E	A	F	T	L
N	L	A	P	G	G	K	L	B	L	A	O	K	J
G	R	R	B	K	V	L	L	O	R	H	G	M	D

Name _____ Class _____ Date _____

Vocabulary and Section Summary B *continued*

SECTION SUMMARY

Read the following section summary.

- In the sexual reproduction of flowering plants, a sperm fertilizes an egg.

- After fertilization, seeds and fruit form. The seeds may sprout into new plants.

- A dormant seed can survive drought and freezing temperatures. Some seeds need extreme conditions to break their dormancy.

- Some plants use plantlets, tubers, or runners to reproduce asexually.

Skills Worksheet

Vocabulary and Section Summary B

Plant Development and Responses
VOCABULARY

After you finish reading the section, try this puzzle! Match the correct description with the correct term. Write the letter in the space provided.

_____ 1. geotropism

_____ 2. deciduous

_____ 3. stimulus

_____ 4. gravitropism

_____ 5. growth

_____ 6. tropism

_____ 7. hormone

_____ 8. evergreen

_____ 9. differentiated

_____ 10. development

_____ 11. phototropism

a. process that an organism goes through as it increases in ability or skill

b. the term used to describe a cell that is specialized to perform a specific function

c. anything that causes a reaction or change in an organism

d. an increase in size

e. a change in the direction a plant grows that is caused by light

f. a tree that loses some of its leaves year-round

g. the growth of all or part of an organism in response to an external stimulus

h. the term used to describe a tree that loses its leaves around the same time each year

i. a chemical that causes cells to react in certain ways

j. a change in the direction of plant growth in response to the direction of gravity

k. another term used to describe gravitropism.

SECTION SUMMARY
Read the following section summary.

Some plant cells are able to differentiate many times in the lifetime of the plant.

There are many groups of plant hormones. Plant hormones can affect a plant's growth and development.

A growth in response to a stimulus is called a tropism. Tropisms are positive or negative.

Plants react to light, gravity, and the change of seasons.

Short-day plants flower when nights are long. Long-day plants flower when nights are short.

Directed Reading B

Section: What Is an Animal? (pp. 424–429)
ANIMAL CHARACTERISTICS

_____ **1.** Until about 200 years ago, people thought sponges were
   a. vertebrates.   **c.** plants.
   b. fungi.   **d.** animals.

_____ **2.** How do animal cells differ from plant cells?
   a. They are larger than plant cells.
   b. Animal cells have cell walls; plant cells do not.
   c. They are made up of different chemical components.
   d. Animal cells are surrounded only by cell membranes.

_____ **3.** All animals are
   a. single celled.
   b. covered in fur.
   c. made up of many cells.
   d. asexual.

_____ **4.** Groups of the same type of cells that work together to perform a specific function are
   a. organ systems.
   b. organs.
   c. muscles.
   d. tissues.

_____ **5.** Into which of the following categories do the heart, lungs, and kidneys fall?
   a. organs
   b. multicellular organisms
   c. tissues
   d. organ systems

_____ **6.** An organ system is a
   a. group of tissues that perform a specific function.
   b. single tissue that performs several functions.
   c. group of organs that perform a specific function.
   d. single organ that performs a specific function.

_____ **7.** A coelom is
   a. a structure found only in plants.
   b. a structure found inside an organ.
   c. a body cavity that protects many organs.
   d. an exoskeleton.

_____ **8.** A sea star
  a. has bilateral symmetry.
  b. has radial symmetry.
  c. has biradial symmetry.
  d. is asymmetrical.

_____ **9.** When an animal's two sides mirror each other, it
  a. has bilateral symmetry.
  b. has radial symmetry.
  c. has biradial symmetry.
  d. is asymmetrical.

_____ **10.** An organism that feeds on other organisms to meet its energy needs is called a
  a. consumer.
  b. producer.
  c. plant
  d. customer.

_____ **11.** For food, mosquitoes
  a. drink nectar.
  b. drink blood.
  c. eat animals.
  d. photosynthesize sunlight.

_____ **12.** The type of reproduction that results in offspring genetically identical to the parent is called
  a. sexual reproduction.
  b. differentiation.
  c. asexual reproduction.
  d. fertilization.

_____ **13.** Two types of asexual reproduction are
  a. budding and fragmentation.
  b. differentiation and fertilization.
  c. egg and differentiation.
  d. sperm and embryo.

_____ **14.** The process of an egg's nucleus joining with a sperm's nucleus is called
  a. budding.
  b. differentiation.
  c. fragmentation.
  d. fertilization.

_____ **15.** What is the process by which cells develop structures according to their function?
    a. reproduction
    b. differentiation
    c. fragmentation
    d. fertilization

_____ **16.** Which of the following is an example of an animal that can move from one place to another at only one stage of its life?
    a. caterpillar
    b. anemone
    c. parrot
    d. nautilus

_____ **17.** An animal that maintains its own body temperature is called a(n)
    a. endotemp.
    b. endotherm.
    c. ectotherm.
    d. exotherm.

_____ **18.** An animal whose body temperature changes with the environment is called a(n)
    a. endotemp.
    b. endotherm.
    c. ectotherm.
    d. exotherm.

19. What are three reasons why animals move?

_____

_____

_____

20. What makes most movement in animals possible?

_____

_____

_____

21. How do birds and mammals maintain their body heat?

_____

_____

_____

Skills Worksheet

Directed Reading B

Section: The Animal Kingdom (pp. 430–437)
ANIMAL DIVERSITY

_____ 1. Scientists have identified
   a. over 1 million species of animals.
   b. over 3 million species of animals.
   c. over 5 million species of animals.
   d. over 1 billion species of animals.

CLASSIFICATION

_____ 2. Scientists do NOT organize animals into groups based on
   a. structure.
   b. personal preference.
   c. evolutionary relationships.
   d. DNA.

_____ 3. All animals, except chordates, fall into what classification?
   a. amphibians
   b. invertebrates
   c. mammals
   d. annelids

INVERTEBRATE CHARACTERISTICS

_____ 4. Which of these body parts is NOT characteristic of invertebrates?
   a. muscles
   b. hair
   c. brain
   d. bones

_____ 5. What are the many tubes and thousands of small holes of a sponge?
   a. eyes
   b. pores
   c. a jelly-like material
   d. glassy structures

_____ 6. The sponge's body plan
   a. has radial symmetry.
   b. has bilateral symmetry.
   c. is symmetrical.
   d. is asymmetrical.

_____ **7.** Unlike flatworms, roundworms have a(n)
- **a.** coelom.
- **b.** endoskeleton.
- **c.** exoskeleton.
- **d.** mantle.

_____ **8.** The body plan of an annelid
- **a.** is asymmetrical.
- **b.** has bilateral symmetry.
- **c.** has radial symmetry.
- **d.** has biradial symmetry.

_____ **9.** Annelids are also called
- **a.** segmented worms.
- **b.** detached worms.
- **c.** vertebrate worms.
- **d.** smooth worms.

_____ **10.** Which of the following are NOT arthropods?
- **a.** crabs
- **b.** shrimp
- **c.** spiders
- **d.** leeches

_____ **11.** Which of the following are NOT echinoderms?
- **a.** crabs
- **b.** sea stars
- **c.** sea urchins
- **d.** sand dollars

12. Why have scientists placed animals they have discovered into groups smaller than species for identification?

_____

_____

_____

13. What are the three major classes of cnidarians?

_____

_____

_____

14. What are the cnidarian's two types of body plan?

_____

_____

15. Describe how the body forms of sea anemones and coral are different in the larval and adult stages.

_____

_____

_____

16. What is a parasite?

_____

_____

17. In what two ways do flatworms reproduce?

_____

_____

Match the correct description with the correct term. Write the letter in the space provided.

_____ **18.** secretes the shells of mollusks

_____ **19.** is used to move

a. muscular foot

b. mantle

20. What are two benefits of an arthropod's exoskeleton?

_____

_____

21. What are four purposes of an echinoderm's water vascular system?

_____

_____

_____

_____

22. What is the process by which echinoderms reproduce sexually?

_____

_____

_____

VERTEBRATE CHARACTERISTICS

_____ **23.** All chordates have a(n)
   a. backbone.
   b. exoskeleton.
   c. notochord.
   d. radially symmetrical body plan.

_____ **24.** A stiff but flexible rod that supports the body of an animal is called a(n)
   a. spine.
   b. notochord.
   c. backbone.
   d. vertebrae.

_____ **25.** A strong but flexible column of individual bony units, or vertebrae, is called a(n)
   a. backbone.
   b. nervous system.
   c. spinal cord.
   d. notochord.

_____ **26.** What is an internal skeleton that is made of bone and cartilage?
   a. backbone
   b. endoskeleton
   c. exoskeleton
   d. shell

_____ **27.** The five main groups of vertebrates are
   a. insects, worms, birds, fish, mammals.
   b. mollusks, annelids, sea urchins, snakes, humans.
   c. fish, amphibians, reptiles, birds, mammals.
   d. insects, reptiles, birds, mammals, humans.

_____ **28.** Most amphibians live near freshwater because
   a. their eggs and larvae need water to survive.
   b. they breathe through gills.
   c. they are dry skinned and need water.
   d. it is the only place to find food.

_____ **29.** Most reptiles live on land because
  a. they cannot swim.
  b. their skin must be kept dry.
  c. they do not need water to lay their eggs.
  d. they all eat other vertebrates.

_____ **30.** Which of the following birds uses its wings to swim?
  a. emu
  b. ostrich
  c. goose
  d. penguin

_____ **31.** Which of the following birds runs instead of flying?
  a. emu
  b. parakeet
  c. goose
  d. penguin

32. How are lancelets different from vertebrates?

_____

_____

_____

Match the correct description with the correct term. Write the letter in the space provided.

_____ **33.** group that includes sharks and stingrays   **a.** bony fish

b. cartilaginous fish
_____ **34.** the largest group of fish

35. What are two characteristics shared by all mammals.

_____

_____

Match the correct description with the correct term. Write the letter in the space provided.

_____ **36.** Offspring develop in shelled eggs.   **a.** placental mammal

b. marsupial
_____ **37.** Offspring develop in a placenta.

c. monotreme
_____ **38.** Offspring develop in the mother's pouch.

Skills Worksheet

Directed Reading B

Section: Invertebrates (pp. 438–443)

INVERTEBRATE CHARACTERISTICS

_____ 1. All invertebrates
    a. absorb nutrients through tissue.
    b. live in water.
    c. lack backbones.
    d. are similar in shape.

_____ 2. Which of the following is NOT a segment of an insect?
    a. head
    b. thorax
    c. abdomen
    d. tail

_____ 3. Which of the following is NOT a body support for an invertebrate?
    a. glassy structures
    b. a backbone
    c. an exoskeleton
    d. thick skin

_____ 4. Which of the following performs respiration in lobsters?
    a. lungs
    b. gills
    c. tracheae
    d. blood

_____ 5. Blood moves through open spaces in the body in a(n)
    a. open circulatory system.
    b. closed circulatory system.
    c. open respiratory system.
    d. closed respiratory system.

_____ 6. An animal digests food in its
    a. circulatory system.
    b. digestive system.
    c. respiratory system.
    d. nervous system.

_____ 7. Which of the following acts as the control center for the nervous system of many animals?
    a. sense organs
    b. nerve
    c. nerve cord
    d. brain

_____ **8.** Which of the following collects information from outside the body?
  a. sense organs
  b. nerve
  c. nerve cord
  d. brain

_____ **9.** Which of the following is a form of reproduction in which a part of the parent organism develops and pinches off to live independently?
  a. budding
  b. fragmentation
  c. sexual
  d. fertilization

_____ **10.** Which of the following is a form of reproduction in which a part of an organism breaks off and develops into an identical individual?
  a. budding
  b. fragmentation
  c. sexual
  d. fertilization

_____ **11.** The process in which some insects shed their exoskeletons as they grow is called
  a. molting.
  b. shedding.
  c. peeling.
  d. warping.

12. Identify three ways in which invertebrates have adapted to their environments.

_____

_____

_____

13. A sponge has an _____ body plan.

14. A sea hare's body plan has _____ symmetry.

15. A jellyfish's body plan has _____ symmetry.

16. Insects have _____ to protect their inner body parts.

17. Animals take in oxygen and release carbon dioxide through

_____ .

18. Some invertebrates have a separate _____ system to eliminate excess water and wastes from cells.

Directed Reading B *continued*

19. List the parts of the digestive system of the snail.

_____

_____

_____

_____

20. What are the four stages of complete metamorphosis?

_____

_____

_____

21. What are the three stages of incomplete metamorphosis?

_____

_____

_____

Skills Worksheet

Directed Reading B

Section: Vertebrates (pp. 444–449)
VERTEBRATE CHARACTERISTICS

_____ **1.** Only vertebrates have
    a. a head.
    b. protein.
    c. tissue.
    d. a backbone.

_____ **2.** The flexible and strong connective tissue found only in vertebrates is called
    a. cartilage.
    b. bone.
    c. skull.
    d. hard tissue.

_____ **3.** The back of a vertebrate is the
    a. dorsal side.
    b. ventral side.
    c. anterior.
    d. posterior.

_____ **4.** The head of a vertebrate is the
    a. dorsal side.
    b. ventral side.
    c. anterior.
    d. posterior.

_____ **5.** Which of the following helps keep a mammal's body temperature stable?
    a. feathers
    b. fur and hair
    c. scales
    d. mucus

_____ **6.** Which of the following helps keep a bird's body temperature stable?
    a. feathers
    b. fur and hair
    c. scales
    d. mucus

_____ **7.** Which of the following is NOT one of the three main parts of an endoskeleton?
  a. backbone
  b. skull
  c. mantle
  d. limb bones

_____ **8.** The main respiratory organs of a fish are the
  a. lungs.
  b. arteries.
  c. gills.
  d. scales.

_____ **9.** The main respiratory organs of land vertebrates are inside the body to
  a. keep them clean
  b. keep them from drying out.
  c. protect them from infection.
  d. provide body support.

_____ **10.** The main respiratory organs of a frog are the
  a. arteries.
  b. scales.
  c. gills.
  d. lungs.

_____ **11.** In vertebrates, blood is pushed through a closed circulatory system by the
  a. lungs.
  b. heart.
  c. blood vessels.
  d. arteries.

_____ **12.** The blood vessels that carry blood to and from the heart are
  a. arteries and veins.
  b. veins and capillaries.
  c. capillaries and veins.
  d. arteries and capillaries.

_____ **13.** The main blood vessels are connected by a network of
  a. arteries.
  b. veins.
  c. capillaries.
  d. pumps.

_____ **14.** The organ in which most food breakdown occurs and nutrients are absorbed is the
    a. small intestine.
    b. large intestine.
    c. kidney.
    d. anus.

_____ **15.** The organ that filters urea from the blood is the
    a. small intestine.
    b. large intestine.
    c. kidney.
    d. anus.

_____ **16.** The organ that turns waste into feces is the
    a. small intestine.
    b. large intestine.
    c. kidney.
    d. anus.

_____ **17.** When sound reaches the ear,
    a. the ear interprets the sound waves.
    b. the ear sends impulses through sensory nerves to the brain.
    c. the ear sends sound waves through the circulatory system.
    d. the ear blocks the sound waves to protect the brain.

_____ **18.** Command impulses are carried from the brain by
    a. arteries.
    b. sensory nerves.
    c. veins.
    d. motor nerves.

_____ **19.** Almost all vertebrates reproduce through
    a. sexual reproduction.
    b. asexual reproduction.
    c. budding.
    d. fragmentation.

_____ **20.** An embryo develops specialized cells through
    a. fusion.
    b. fertilization.
    c. differentiation.
    d. metamorphosis.

_____ **21.** Fish and amphibian larvae
    a. hatch on land.
    b. can reproduce.
    c. can't reproduce.
    d. are exactly the same as adults.

_____ **22.** Animals that have a larval stage in their life cycle include
    a. reptiles.
    b. amphibians.
    c. birds.
    d. mammals.

_____ **23.** Parenting skills of birds and mammals differ from those of fish and reptiles in that
    a. fish and reptiles parent until their offspring are adults.
    b. birds and mammals have fewer offspring, so they parent longer.
    c. fish and reptiles have fewer offspring, so they parent longer.
    d. only birds and mammals abandon their offspring at birth.

24. What happens to the cartilage of most vertebrate embryos as they grow?

_____

_____

25. What unique purpose is served by the mucous covering on the bodies of amphibians?

_____

_____

26. How does the respiratory system in fish work?

_____

_____

_____

27. Describe how the circulatory system and respiratory system in a land vertebrate work together.

_____

_____

_____

_____

28. How do animals with larger brains differ from those with smaller brains?

_____

_____

_____

Name _____ Class _____ Date _____

Vocabulary and Section Summary B

What Is an Animal?

VOCABULARY

After you finish reading the section, try this puzzle! Use the clues below to solve the crossword puzzle on the following page.

ACROSS

1. Animals called _____ rely on their environment to maintain their body temperature.

8. _____ are birds and mammals that maintain their own body temperatures by using some of the energy released by chemical reactions.

9. Reproduction in which parts of an organism break off and then develop into new individuals is known as _____.

11. A body cavity or _____ contains the internal organs of some organisms.

DOWN

2. _____ occurs when sex cells from two parents combine to form offspring.

3. A(n) _____ is a group of organs that work together to perform a specific function.

4. An organism that is _____ is made up of many cells.

5. An organism that eats other organisms or organic matter is a(n) _____.

6. In the process of _____, the structure and function of the parts of an organism change to enable specialization of those parts.

7. An organism that is a(n) _____ is in one of the early stages of development.

10. When an organism reproduces by _____, one of its parts develops into a new organism.

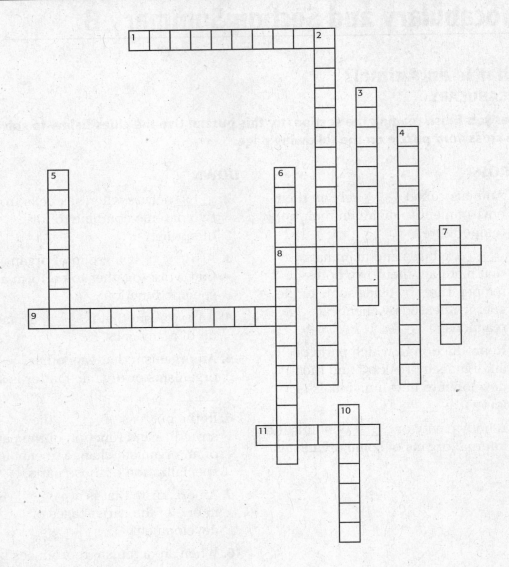

SECTION SUMMARY

Read the following section summary.

- All animals are multicellular organisms. Specialized cells in animals are organized into tissues, organs, and organ systems.

- Most animals have bilateral symmetry or radial symmetry. Some are asymmetrical.

- Animals consume other organisms to get energy.

- Animals reproduce asexually or sexually.

- As an embryo develops, its cells differentiate.

- Animals move in many ways.

- Animals that maintain their own body temperature are endotherms. Animals that rely on their environment to maintain their body temperature are ectotherms.

Name _____ Class _____ Date _____

Skills Worksheet

Vocabulary and Section Summary B

The Animal Kingdom
VOCABULARY

After you finish reading the section, try this puzzle! In the space provided, write the erm described. Then, find the words in the word search puzzle on the next page. erms can be hidden in the puzzle vertically, horizontally, diagonally, or backward.

_____ 1. an animal that does not have a backbone

_____ 2. a hard, external, supporting structure for an animal

_____ 3. an animal that has a backbone

_____ 4. an internal skeleton made of bone and cartilage

_____ 5. small holes in the body of a sponge

_____ 6. a cup or bell-shaped body that has tentacles extending from it

_____ 7. a specialized tissue that secretes the shell of snails, clams, and oysters

_____ 8. a name that means "spiny skinned"

_____ 9. a stiff but flexible rod that supports the body of a chordate

_____ 10. individual bony units that make up the backbone of an animal

_____ 11. an organ through which nutrients and wastes are exchanged between the mother and developing offspring

X	G	H	H	S	F	P	F	E	R	G	S	H	E	S	S	I	M	B	J	Q
C	S	Z	X	D	S	Y	U	I	T	O	P	E	N	G	C	J	C	J	O	O
Q	O	L	U	E	H	W	B	V	S	A	I	Q	H	S	T	K	X	I	Q	Q
B	R	J	R	U	H	A	E	F	R	O	R	A	T	N	E	C	A	L	P	N
E	P	O	F	S	M	R	T	Y	H	U	E	B	Y	P	D	M	C	H	O	O
I	P	P	O	H	T	A	D	L	C	J	E	G	E	F	W	J	V	T	M	T
P	Y	R	U	E	J	E	U	D	W	A	I	F	L	T	A	O	E	I	C	E
C	Z	H	B	N	P	U	C	Z	J	T	U	B	E	K	R	L	U	J	O	L
G	Z	R	A	I	F	O	J	H	G	V	U	Q	X	S	E	E	T	C	V	E
E	A	J	Y	O	S	N	Q	J	I	V	A	Q	F	K	E	A	V	G	V	K
E	J	G	R	O	D	T	H	X	V	N	S	S	S	K	B	T	N	N	Y	S
G	P	Z	C	K	Q	S	M	Y	H	B	O	O	U	Y	L	I	O	O	I	O
P	V	E	R	T	E	B	R	A	T	E	X	D	T	D	N	Y	Z	T	A	D
V	W	I	H	I	L	S	U	F	G	E	Z	H	E	D	E	R	I	O	U	N
T	C	X	L	P	T	J	I	Q	E	I	Y	L	T	R	T	M	E	C	K	E
B	W	A	Z	A	N	J	A	B	R	L	L	B	F	X	M	L	I	H	O	O
J	H	I	W	U	A	V	Z	R	W	J	B	S	E	N	G	H	F	O	U	O
C	J	T	K	R	M	Q	K	Y	X	Q	C	L	A	O	P	G	T	R	O	E
X	A	N	H	E	F	T	Q	D	X	B	V	Q	W	K	K	A	J	D	C	X
N	L	D	F	L	K	S	O	Q	O	J	L	O	B	H	B	L	P	S	J	K

SECTION SUMMARY

Read the following section summary.

- The animal kingdom can be divided into two main groups: invertebrates and vertebrates. Invertebrates do not have backbones. Vertebrates have backbones.

- Sponges, cnidarians, flatworms, roundworms, mollusks, annelids, arthropods, and echinoderms are groups of invertebrates.

- Fish, amphibians, reptiles, birds, and mammals are groups of vertebrates.

- Invertebrate bodies can be asymmetrical, radially symmetrical, or bilaterally symmetrical. Some invertebrates have different body symmetries at different stages in their life cycle.

- Most vertebrate bodies have bilateral symmetry.

- Many invertebrates reproduce by asexual reproduction and sexual reproduction. Most vertebrates reproduce only by sexual reproduction.

Name _____ Class _____ Date _____

Vocabulary and Section Summary B

Invertebrates

VOCABULARY

After you finish reading the section, try this puzzle! Use the clues below to unscramble the letters, and write the word in the space provided.

1. any part of a larger structure, such as the body of an organism, that is set off by natural or arbitrary boundaries: EEGSTMN

_____

2. a circulatory system in which the circulatory fluid is not contained entirely within vessels: LESTMYCICESAYNTROUPOR

_____

3. a circulatory system in which the heart circulates blood through a network of vessels that form a closed loop: UCCYTAYROSLRLSMICDOSEET

_____

4. a process in the life cycle of many animals during which a rapid change from the immature organism to the adult takes place: SMOPROASHETMI

_____

5. in insects, a network of tubes inside the body that performs respiration: ARCHEAT

_____

6. specialized areas of the nervous system that collect information from outside and inside the body: ENSSE ONRGAS

_____

7. a specialized area of the nervous system that acts as the control center of the functions of the body: NRABI

_____

8. a process in which some insects shed their exoskeleton several times: GNOMLTI

_____

SECTION SUMMARY

Read the following section summary.

- Invertebrate bodies are asymmetrical, have radial symmetry, or bilateral symmetry.

- The bodies of many invertebrates are divided into segments.

- Invertebrates have protective outer coverings that provide support and serve as a place for muscles to attach.

- Invertebrates may have many basic organ systems, such as a respiratory system, a circulatory system, a digestive system, an excretory system, a nervous system, and a reproductive system.

- Invertebrates reproduce asexually and sexually. Invertebrates develop from embryos into larvae and from larvae into adults.

Skills Worksheet

Vocabulary and Section Summary B

Vertebrates

VOCABULARY

After you finish reading the section, try this puzzle! Use the clues below to write the terms being described in the blanks on the next page. Then, write the boxed letters in the space provided to spell out a phrase related to animals.

1. a flexible and strong connective tissue

2. nerves that carry impulses from the body to the brain

3. the wider and shorter portion of the intestine that removes water from mostly digested food and turns the waste into semisolid feces, or stool

4. nerves that carry command impulses throughout the body from the brain

5. the organ between the stomach and the large intestine where most of the breakdown of food happens and most of the nutrients from food are absorbed

6. vessels that carry blood to the heart

7. the front of the body of a vertebrate

8. the upper body surface or back of a vertebrate

9. vessels that carry blood away from the heart

10. the back of the body of a vertebrate

11. the lower surface or belly of a vertebrate

1. _ _ ☐ _ _ _ _ _ _ _ _

2. _ _ _ _ _ _ _ _ ☐ _ _ _ _ _

3. _ _ _ _ _ ☐ _ _ _ _ _ _ _

4. ☐ _ _ _ _ _ _ _ _ _

5. _ _ ☐ _ ☐ _ _ _ _ _ _ _

6. _ _ _ _ ☐

7. ☐ _ _ _ _ _ _ _ _

8. ☐ _ _ _ _ _

9. ☐ _ _ _ _ _ _ _

10. ☐ _ _ _ _ _ _ _ _

11. _ _ _ ☐ _ _ _

12. What is the phrase?

_ _ _ _ _ _ _ _   _ _ _ _ _ _

SECTION SUMMARY

Read the following section summary.

- Skin protects the body from the environment. Skin of vertebrates may be covered in scales, feathers, or fur.

- Most vertebrates have an endoskeleton made of bone. The endoskeleton provides support, protection, and a place for muscles to attach.

- Major organ systems of vertebrates are the respiratory system, circulatory system, digestive system, excretory system, nervous system, and reproductive system.

- Cells of embryos differentiate and specialize as the embryo develops.

- The amount of parental care given to offspring varies among species of vertebrates.

Directed Reading B

Section: Body Organization (pp. 466–471)
A STABLE INTERNAL ENVIRONMENT

1. The maintenance of a stable internal environment in the body is

_____.

CELLS, TISSUES, AND ORGANS

_____ **2.** What is a collection of tissues that work together to carry out a specialized function in the body?
   a. a cell
   b. connective tissue
   c. an organ
   d. a team

_____ **3.** Muscle tissue helps your stomach digest food by
   a. protecting the stomach.
   b. supplying oxygen.
   c. breaking up food.
   d. producing acids.

4. What can happen to cells if homeostasis is disrupted?

_____

_____

5. How is your body like a soccer team?

_____

_____

_____

6. A group of similar cells working together forms

a(n) _____.

Directed Reading B *continued*

Match the correct description with the correct term. Write the letter in the space provided.

_____ **7.** joins, supports, and insulates organs

_____ **8.** covers and protects underlying tissue

_____ **9.** sends electrical signals through the body

_____ **10.** produces movement

a. nervous tissue
b. muscle tissue
c. epithelial tissue
d. connective tissue

11. The wall of the stomach contains blood, a(n) _____ tissue.

12. The inside of your stomach is lined with _____.

13. Organs that work together make up _____

ORGAN SYSTEMS WORKING TOGETHER

Match the correct description with the correct term. Write the letter in the space provided.

_____ **14.** includes the heart, blood vessels, and blood

_____ **15.** removes wastes from blood

_____ **16.** sends out chemical messages

_____ **17.** includes skin, hair, and nails

_____ **18.** supports and protects body parts

_____ **19.** helps get rid of bacteria and viruses

_____ **20.** absorbs oxygen through the lungs

_____ **21.** breaks down food into nutrients

_____ **22.** helps the body move

_____ **23.** produces eggs and protects the fetus

_____ **24.** sends and receives electrical messages throughout the body

a. integumentary system
b. muscular system
c. skeletal system
d. cardiovascular system
e. respiratory system
f. urinary system
g. female reproductive system
h. nervous system
i. digestive system
j. lymphatic system
k. endocrine system

25. How do organ systems work together to maintain homeostasis? Give an example.

_____

_____

26. What effect may the failure of an organ have on other organ systems? Give an example.

_____

_____

_____

_____

Skills Worksheet

Directed Reading B

Section: The Skeletal System (pp. 472–475)

1. Your skeletal system is made up of _____,

_____, and the _____ that holds

bones together.

BONES

_____ 2. When you were born, most of your skeleton was made of
   a. compact bone.
   b. cartilage.
   c. spongy bone.
   d. osteoblasts.

_____ 3. What are two parts of your body that are made out of cartilage?
   a. hair and nails
   b. ear lobes and jaw bone
   c. teeth and gums
   d. end of nose and top of ear

4. What are the four functions of the skeletal system?

_____

_____

_____

_____

5. The part of the skeletal system that protects the heart and lungs is

the _____.

6. Bones store _____.

7. Some of your bones are filled with a special material called

_____, which makes blood cells.

8. The minerals found in bones are deposited by living cells

called _____.

Identify the type of bone tissue to which each of the following descriptions relates. Write *compact bone* or *spongy bone* in the space provided.

_____ **9.** It has many open spaces.

_____ **10.** It is rigid and dense.

_____ **11.** It contains small blood vessels.

_____ **12.** It provides most of the strength for bones.

13. Compare red bone marrow and yellow bone marrow.

_____

_____

JOINTS

Match the correct description with the correct term. Write the letter in the space provided.

_____ **14.** allows little or no movement

_____ **15.** allows movement in all directions

_____ **16.** allows you to flex and extend

_____ **17.** cushions the area where bones meet

_____ **18.** where two or more bones meet

_____ **19.** connective tissue that connects the bones in a joint

_____ **20.** the type of joint found in the hand and wrist

a. gliding joint
b. ligaments
c. fixed joint
d. joint
e. hinge joint
f. ball-and-socket joint
g. cartilage

SKELETAL SYSTEM INJURIES AND DISEASES

21. Explain how parts of the skeletal system may become injured.

_____

_____

_____

22. A disease that causes bones to become less dense is

called _____.

23. A disease that may cause joints to swell or stiffen is

called _____.

Skills Worksheet

Directed Reading B

Section: The Muscular System (pp. 476–481)

1. Why is it impossible for your body to not move any muscles at all?

_____

_____

_____

KINDS OF MUSCLE

Match the correct description with the correct term. Write the letter in the space provided.

_____ **2.** found in your heart and pumps blood around your body

_____ **3.** enables your bones to move

_____ **4.** found in the digestive tract and in the walls of blood vessels

a. smooth muscle

b. cardiac muscle

c. skeletal muscle

5. Muscle action that is under your control is _____.

6. Muscle action that is not under your control is _____.

MOVEMENT

7. What happens in your body when you want to move?

_____

_____

_____

8. Tendons are strands of connective tissue that connect your

_____ to your _____.

9. A muscle that bends part of your body is called

a(n) _____.

10. A muscle that straightens part of your body is called

a(n) _____.

11. When your arm bends, the _____ muscle is the flexor.

12. When your arm straightens, the _____ muscle is the extensor.

LEVERS IN THE HUMAN BODY

_____ **13.** In a first-class lever,
    a. the load is between the fulcrum and the effort force.
    b. the fulcrum is between the effort force and the load.
    c. the effort force is between the fulcrum and the load.
    d. there is no fulcrum.

_____ **14.** In a second-class lever,
    a. the load is between the fulcrum and the effort force.
    b. the fulcrum is between the effort force and the load.
    c. the effort force is between the fulcrum and the load.
    d. there is no fulcrum.

_____ **15.** In a third-class lever,
    a. the load is between the fulcrum and the effort force.
    b. the fulcrum is between the effort force and the load.
    c. the effort force is between the fulcrum and the load.
    d. there is no fulcrum.

16. A(n) _____ is a rigid bar that pivots at a fixed point called

a(n) _____ .

17. A force applied to a lever is called a(n) _____ ,

while a force that resists the motion of a lever is called

a(n) _____ .

18. The increase in work that can be done by using a lever is called

a(n) _____ .

USE IT OR LOSE IT

19. How does having strong muscles benefit the rest of the body?

_____

_____

_____

_____

20. Skeletal muscles can be strengthened by doing _____ .

21. When you do resistance exercise, you work against the resistance,

or _____, of an object.

22. What are some examples of aerobic exercise?

_____

_____

23. Endurance can be increased by doing _____.

MUSCLE INJURY

_____ **24.** A strain is an injury in which a muscle or tendon is
- **a.** fractured or broken.
- **b.** overstretched or torn.
- **c.** swollen or inflamed.
- **d.** dislocated or moved.

_____ **25.** Tendinitis is a condition in which a tendon becomes
- **a.** less dense.
- **b.** bruised.
- **c.** rested.
- **d.** inflamed.

26. What are the dangers of taking anabolic steroids?

_____

_____

_____

Skills Worksheet

Vocabulary and Section Summary B

Body Organization
VOCABULARY

After you finish reading the section, try this puzzle! Use the clues given to fill in the blanks below. Then, copy the numbered letters into the corresponding boxes on the following page to reveal the four kinds of tissue.

1. the maintenance of a stable environment inside the body

___ ___ ___ ___ ___ ___ ___ ___ ___ ___ ___
  10   4   6

2. a type of cell that has unique structures specialized to perform specific functions

___ ___ ___ ___ ___ ___ ___ ___ ___ ___ ___ ___ ___ ___
   8   1

3. a group of similar cells that perform a common function

___ ___ ___ ___ ___ ___
  9   5

4. a collection of tissues that perform a specialized function of the body

___ ___ ___ ___ ___
    3

5. a group of organs that work together

___ ___ ___ ___ ___   ___ ___ ___ ___ ___ ___
      11   2   7

What are the four kinds of body tissue?

a. tissue that sends electrical signals throughout the body

___ ___ ___ V ___ ___ ___
 1   2   3   4   5   6

b. tissue that contracts and relaxes to produce movement

___ ___ ___ C L ___
 7   5   6   2

c. tissue that covers and protects underlying tissue

___ P ___ ___ ___ ___ ___ L ___ ___ L
 2   8   9 10 2   8 11

d. tissue that joins, supports, protects, insulates, nourishes, and cushions organs

C ___ ___ ___ ___ C ___ ___ V ___
  4   1   1   2   9   8   2

SECTION SUMMARY

Read the following section summary.

- A human has many levels of organization.

- Most human cells are differentiated in structure for specific functions, or jobs, within the body.

- A group of cells that work together is a tissue. Tissues form organs. Organs that work together form organ systems.

- There are four kinds of tissue in the human body.

- There are 11 organ systems in the human body.

- Organ systems work together to help the body maintain homeostasis.

Skills Worksheet

Vocabulary and Section Summary B

The Skeletal System
VOCABULARY

After you finish reading the section, try this puzzle! Use the clues to solve the crossword puzzle below.

ACROSS

3. disease in which the bones become less dense

4. flexible tissue that can turn into bone

5. group of organs that protect, support, and move the body (two words)

7. the type of bone tissue that gives a bone strength and support (two words)

8. the type of bone tissue that is rigid and dense (two words)

9. a disease that affects the joints

DOWN

1. special material in bone that makes blood cells

2. a place where two or more bones meet

3. cells that deposit minerals that create bone

5. occurs when a ligament is stretched too far or torn

6. a strong elastic band that holds a joint together

Vocabulary and Section Summary B *continued*

SECTION SUMMARY

Read the following section summary.

- The skeletal system includes bones, cartilage, and the connective tissue that connects bones.

- Bones protect the body, store minerals, allow movement, and make blood cells.

- A joint is a place where two or more bones meet.

- Skeletal system injuries include fractures, dislocations, and sprains. Skeletal system diseases include osteoporosis and arthritis.

Skills Worksheet

Vocabulary and Section Summary B

The Muscular System
VOCABULARY

After you finish reading the section, try this puzzle! Use the clues below to fill in the correct term. Then, find the words in the word search on the next page. Words in the puzzle are hidden vertically, horizontally, forward, backward, and diagonally.

_____ **1.** a bar that pivots at a fixed point

_____ **2.** steady, moderately intense activity

_____ **3.** effort force is between the fulcrum and the load

_____ **4.** muscle action under your control

_____ **5.** muscle that straightens part of the body

_____ **6.** force applied to a lever

_____ **7.** connect skeletal muscles to bones

_____ **8.** muscle found in the digestive tract

_____ **9.** muscle action not under your control

_____ **10.** muscle that bends part of the body

_____ **11.** muscle found in the heart

_____ **12.** force that resists the motion of a lever

_____ **13.** made up of the muscles that let you move

_____ **14.** caused when an injured tendon is inflamed during exercise

_____ **15.** how many times a machine multiplies force

_____ **16.** the load is between the fulcrum and effort force

_____ **17.** fixed pivot point on a lever

_____ **18.** the fulcrum is between the effort force and load

_____ **19.** an injury in which a muscle or tendon is over-stretched or torn

Vocabulary and Section Summary B *continued*

F	I	R	S	T	C	L	A	S	S	L	E	V	E	R	E	R	Z	S	N
G	G	F	I	S	M	B	E	L	Y	T	E	N	D	O	N	S	R	M	B
B	A	E	I	R	X	J	Q	V	N	H	X	T	T	C	Z	E	S	O	Q
R	O	X	E	L	F	T	U	M	E	I	E	S	H	U	V	J	M	E	F
H	N	T	N	K	E	T	Y	R	E	R	L	S	V	E	P	N	O	S	R
K	A	E	S	N	I	R	C	C	F	D	A	O	L	C	R	W	O	I	O
E	V	N	S	D	G	X	T	L	Y	C	J	S	L	V	A	R	T	C	F
Y	D	S	W	Q	V	J	Z	K	A	L	S	U	X	H	F	M	H	R	E
R	H	O	T	I	Y	S	L	Y	R	A	N	F	B	J	K	K	M	E	L
A	L	R	J	L	F	N	O	X	L	S	S	T	R	E	T	C	U	X	C
T	A	N	N	S	Z	C	P	C	N	S	M	L	T	N	O	F	S	E	S
N	C	F	M	H	K	Y	D	X	I	L	F	U	E	U	Y	I	C	C	U
U	I	G	P	C	D	N	A	D	A	E	L	O	R	V	F	S	L	I	M
L	N	E	N	O	O	F	L	J	R	V	F	O	V	C	E	S	E	B	C
O	A	Z	H	C	B	C	A	X	T	E	J	T	H	L	L	R	T	O	A
V	H	F	E	M	E	T	S	Y	S	R	A	L	U	C	S	U	M	R	I
N	C	S	N	W	B	X	L	E	C	R	O	F	T	R	O	F	F	E	D
I	E	Y	O	A	V	O	L	U	N	T	A	R	Y	S	X	K	O	A	R
E	G	A	T	N	A	V	D	A	L	A	C	I	N	A	H	C	E	M	A
M	S	I	T	I	N	I	D	N	E	T	U	S	F	I	K	I	V	I	C

SECTION SUMMARY

Read the following section summary.

- The three kinds of muscle tissue are smooth muscle, cardiac muscle, and skeletal muscle.

- Skeletal muscles work in pairs. Skeletal muscles contract to move bones.

- Muscles and bones work together to form levers.

- There are three classes of levers in the human body. Levers work to provide some advantage to body movements.

- First- and second-class levers increase the amount of force applied to a load. Third-class levers increase the speed of the motion.

- Strains are injuries that affect muscles and tendons. Tendinitis affects tendons.

Name _____ Class _____ Date _____

Skills Worksheet

Directed Reading B

Section: The Cardiovascular System (pp. 496–501)

1. The word *cardio* means _____.

2. The word *vascular* means _____.

3. Arteries, veins, and capillaries are _____ that carry blood pumped by the heart.

YOUR CARDIOVASCULAR SYSTEM

4. The heart, blood, and blood vessels together make up

the _____.

5. What are three examples of how the cardiovascular system helps maintain homeostasis?

_____

_____

_____

THE HEART

_____ **6.** What kind of tissue makes up most of the heart?
   a. vascular   **c.** circulatory
   b. cardiac   **d.** lymphatic

_____ **7.** Each upper chamber of the heart is called a(n)
   a. atrium.
   b. ventricle.
   c. valve.
   d. cardio.

_____ **8.** Each lower chamber of the heart is called a(n)
   a. atrium.
   b. ventricle.
   c. valve.
   d. cardio.

_____ **9.** The right side of the heart pumps oxygen-poor blood to the
   a. body.
   b. lungs.
   c. right ventricle.
   d. left atrium.

Directed Reading B continued

_____ **10.** The left side of the heart pumps oxygen-rich blood to the
   a. body.
   b. lungs.
   c. right ventricle.
   d. left atrium.

_____ **11.** When atria relax, what do ventricles do?
   a. expand
   b. relax
   c. contract
   d. close

12. Why do the heart's valves close?

_____

_____

13. What part of the heart makes the heartbeat sound?

_____

_____

BLOOD VESSELS

Use the terms from the following list to complete the sentences below.

capillaries   arteries   blood vessels
veins   pulse

14. Blood vessels that carry blood away from the heart are

_____.

15. Blood vessels that allow exchanges between blood and cells are

_____.

16. Blood vessels that carry blood to the heart are _____.

17. Your _____ is caused by rhythmic

changes in your blood pressure.

18. Blood travels through your body in hollow tubes called

_____.

19. What is the narrowest kind of blood vessel?

_____

20. What kind of blood vessels are helped by the contracting of skeletal muscles?

_____

21. What kind of blood vessels stretch due to blood pressure?

_____

WO TYPES OF CIRCULATION

_____ **22.** What enters the blood when it is pumped to the lungs?
   a. blood vessels
   b. capillaries
   c. oxygen
   d. carbon dioxide

_____ **23.** What leaves the blood when it is pumped to the lungs?
   a. blood vessels
   b. capillaries
   c. oxygen
   d. carbon dioxide

_____ **24.** Where does the exchange of blood and oxygen take place in the lungs?
   a. ventricles
   b. arteries
   c. capillaries
   d. veins

25. The flow of blood between the heart and the lungs is

_____ circulation.

26. The flow of blood between the heart and the rest of the body

is _____ circulation.

CARDIOVASCULAR PROBLEMS

27. Cardiovascular problems can harm the whole _____.

28. A healthy diet and plenty of _____ can reduce the risk
of cardiovascular problems.

29. What is the leading cause of death in the United States?

_____

_____

Name _____ Class _____ Date _____

Directed Reading B *continued*

Match the correct description with the correct term. Write the letter in the space provided. Some terms will not be used.

_____ **30.** fatty buildup in blood vessels

_____ **31.** abnormally high blood pressure

_____ **32.** brain damage caused by damage to blood vessels

_____ **33.** condition caused by the death of heart muscle cells

a. blood poisoning

b. heart failure

c. heart attack

d. atherosclerosis

e. stroke

f. hypertension

34. What can happen when blood supply to the heart is blocked?

_____

_____

_____

Skills Worksheet

Directed Reading B

Section: Blood (pp. 502–507)

1. An adult body has about _____ liters of blood.

COMPONENTS OF BLOOD

2. List the four components of blood.

_____

_____

_____

_____

3. The fluid part of blood is called _____.

4. What do red blood cells do?

_____

_____

5. To what does hemoglobin attach?

_____

6. When bleeding starts, _____ form a plug to reduce blood loss.

7. What two things do white blood cells do?

_____

_____

8. Pathogens include bacteria, _____, and other microscopic organisms.

9. To fight pathogens, white blood cells destroy pathogens or release _____.

10. What destroys dead or damaged body cells?

_____

_____

BODY TEMPERATURE REGULATION

11. Blood helps to regulate body _____.

12. When body temperature rises, blood vessels in the skin

_____.

BLOOD PRESSURE

_____ **13.** The force that blood exerts on the walls of the arteries is called
   a. systolic pressure.
   b. blood pressure.
   c. contraction.
   d. diastolic pressure.

14. When is systolic pressure measured?

_____

_____

15. When is diastolic pressure measured?

_____

_____

16. What are two organs that can be damaged by high blood pressure?

_____

_____

BLOOD TYPES

_____ **17.** To what does a blood type refer?
   a. blood pressure levels
   b. antibodies
   c. blood color and consistency
   d. chemicals called antigens on red blood cells

_____ **18.** What kind of antibodies does a person with type A blood have?
   a. type A
   b. type B
   c. type O
   d. type A and type B

19. How do type B antibodies react to type B antigens?

_____

_____

_____

20. What can happen if an RH⁻ person receives RH⁺ blood?

_____

_____

_____

TRANSFUSIONS AND BLOOD TYPES

_____ **21.** A person with which blood type can donate blood to people of any other blood type?
   a. A
   b. B
   c. AB
   d. O

22. What does a transfusion attempt to replace?

_____

_____

_____

BLOOD DISORDERS

23. What are two common blood disorders?

_____

_____

Skills Worksheet

Directed Reading B

Section: The Respiratory System (pp. 508–511)

1. Your body needs oxygen in order to get _____ from the food you eat.

RESPIRATION AND THE RESPIRATORY SYSTEM

Match the correct description with the correct term. Write the letter in the space provided.

_____ 2. area of the throat that contains the vocal chords

_____ 3. group of organs that take in oxygen and get rid of carbon dioxide

_____ 4. main passage into and out of the respiratory system

_____ 5. throat

_____ 6. tube guarded by the larynx

_____ 7. tube that connects the trachea to the lungs

_____ 8. smaller branches of bronchi

_____ 9. tiny sacs at the ends of the bronchioles

a. larynx

b. nose

c. pharynx

d. respiratory system

e. alveoli

f. bronchioles

g. bronchus

h. trachea

Match the correct description with the correct term. Write the letter in the space provided.

_____ 10. process of using oxygen and releasing carbon dioxide and water

_____ 11. inhalation and exhalation

_____ 12. use of oxygen by cells to release energy stored in food

a. breathing

b. respiration

c. cellular respiration

BREATHING

13. List the two kinds of muscle involved with breathing.

_____

_____

14. When you inhale, the _____ contracts.

15. When the diaphragm contracts, the _____ contract and lift the rib cage.

BREATHING AND CELLULAR RESPIRATION

16. When you inhale, you take in _____.

17. Oxygen diffuses into _____.

18. When the oxygen is carried to cells, it is used to release

_____.

19. Cellular respiration produces water and _____.

RESPIRATORY DISORDERS

_____ **20.** Asthma can be triggered by
   a. blood cells.
   b. dust or pollen.
   c. antigens.
   d. SARS.

_____ **21.** SARS is caused by
   a. dust or pollen.
   b. a virus.
   c. bacteria.
   d. asthma.

22. People with respiratory disorders may have trouble getting rid of

_____.

Skills Worksheet

Vocabulary and Section Summary B

The Cardiovascular System
VOCABULARY

After you finish reading the section, try this puzzle! Use the clues below to fill in the correct terms. Then, complete the word search puzzle on the next page. Words may appear horizontally, vertically, diagonally, or backward.

_____ **1.** system that transports materials to and from the body's cells

_____ **2.** type of blood circulation between the heart and the lungs

_____ **3.** the smallest blood vessels in the body

_____ **4.** type of blood circulation between the heart and the rest of the body

_____ **5.** blood vessels that direct blood away from the heart

_____ **6.** blood vessels that direct blood toward the heart

G	L	Y	M	X	A	T	I	C	I	M	E	T	S	Y	S	A	M
T	I	A	L	V	E	E	L	I	T	O	L	N	M	O	V	L	O
O	B	S	U	R	D	S	H	U	O	C	T	E	F	O	S	X	S
N	E	L	A	O	E	C	P	A	B	C	A	C	L	Q	Y	M	C
S	H	T	G	I	N	T	H	Y	T	A	P	L	I	M	R	P	A
I	I	L	R	O	X	Y	L	N	D	R	X	N	Y	R	A	H	P
L	B	A	R	O	D	D	T	B	I	D	I	T	R	E	N	N	I
S	I	B	L	B	I	P	C	Y	G	I	S	A	O	S	O	O	L
E	B	M	A	R	A	L	R	S	U	O	B	O	T	P	M	G	L
L	M	L	H	R	P	A	H	E	E	V	I	X	A	I	L	E	A
C	A	H	G	J	H	T	U	I	S	A	R	L	P	K	U	S	R
I	W	R	O	R	R	E	M	R	P	S	C	S	D	T	P	U	I
R	X	N	H	R	A	L	E	E	L	C	U	B	P	R	S	I	E
T	C	T	V	S	Y	E	Y	T	E	U	P	R	S	I	E	U	S
T	C	A	N	D	M	T	K	R	E	L	I	E	E	O	S	S	R
E	P	E	M	L	A	S	M	A	N	A	Y	M	L	N	T	E	I
V	E	I	N	S	U	Z	Y	H	T	R	A	Z	H	E	A	S	N

SECTION SUMMARY

Read the following section summary.

Parts of the cardiovascular system include the heart, three types of blood vessels, and blood.

Contractions of the heart pump blood throughout the body. Valves ensure that blood flows in only one direction.

The three types of blood vessels are arteries, veins, and capillaries.

Oxygen-poor blood flows from the heart through the lungs, where it picks up oxygen. Oxygen-rich blood flows from the heart to the rest of the body.

Cardiovascular problems include atherosclerosis, hypertension, strokes, heart attacks, and heart failure.

Skills Worksheet)

Vocabulary and Section Summary B

Blood
VOCABULARY

After you finish reading the section, try this puzzle! Use the clues below to solve the crossword puzzle on the following page.

ACROSS

2. force that blood exerts on the walls of arteries (two words)

5. disease in which blood does not clot normally

7. a cancer that affects blood cells

8. fluid that carries gases, nutrients, and wastes throughout the body

11. type of cells that destroy pathogens (three words)

14. chemicals that identify or destroy pathogens

DOWN

1. pressure inside arteries when ventricles contract

3. bacteria, viruses, and other microscopic particles that can make you sick

4. type of cells that carry oxygen throughout the body

5. an oxygen-carrying protein

6. type of molecule on the surface of red blood cells

9. occurs when a person's cells do not get enough blood

10. pieces of larger cells found in bone marrow

12. injection of blood or blood components into a person

13. pressure inside arteries when ventricles relax

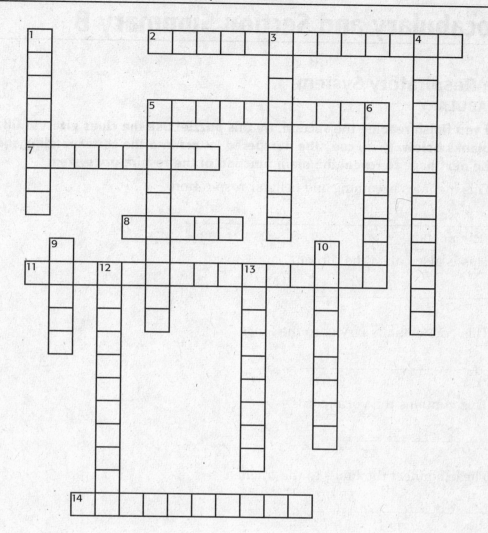

SECTION SUMMARY

Read the following section summary.

The four main components of blood are plasma, red blood cells, platelets, and white blood cells.

Blood carries oxygen and nutrients to cells, helps protect against disease, and helps regulate body temperature.

Blood pressure is the force that blood exerts on the inside walls of arteries. It is often expressed in the unit of millimeters of mercury.

Every person has one of four ABO blood types.

Losing blood, mixing blood types, and blood disorders can be fatal.

Name _____ Class _____ Date _____

Skills Worksheet

Vocabulary and Section Summary B

The Respiratory System
VOCABULARY

After you finish reading the section, try this puzzle! Use the clues given to fill in the blanks below. Then, copy the numbered letters into the corresponding squares on the next page to reveal the main function of the respiratory system.

1. This includes breathing and cellular respiration.

___ ___ ___ ___ ___ ___ ___ ___ ___
22 3 18   29   21   25 24 12

2. This is also called the throat.

___ ___ ___ ___ ___
      13   5 28

3. This connects the larynx to the lungs.

___ ___ ___ ___ ___ ___
1   20   9 11

4. This contains the vocal cords.

___ ___ ___ ___ ___
      25 7

5. These connect the lungs to the trachea.

___ ___ ___ ___ ___ ___
23   10

6. This organ system includes the pharynx, larynx, trachea, and lungs.

___ ___ ___ ___ ___ ___ ___ ___
19   4   6   8

___ ___ ___ ___ ___
16   30

7. These are tiny air sacs in the lungs.

___ ___ ___ ___ ___ ___
2 15   14 27   26

Copyright © by Holt, Rinehart and Winston. All rights reserved.

Holt California Life Science   **248**   Circulation and Respiration

8. What is the main function of the respiratory system?

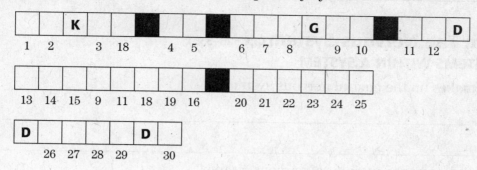

SECTION SUMMARY

Read the following section summary.

Air enters through the nose or mouth, then travels to the pharynx, larynx, trachea, and bronchi. The bronchi branch into bronchioles, which branch into alveoli.

Breathing involves lungs, muscles in the rib cage, and the diaphragm.

Oxygen enters the blood through the alveoli in the lungs. Carbon dioxide leaves the blood and is exhaled.

Respiratory disorders include asthma, emphysema, and SARS.

Skills Worksheet

Directed Reading B

Section: The Nervous System (pp. 526–533)
TWO SYSTEMS WITHIN A SYSTEM

1. What makes up the central nervous system?

_____

_____

2. What makes up the peripheral nervous system?

_____

_____

Mark each of the following statements *P* for peripheral nervous system or *C* for central nervous system.

_____ **3.** includes nerves

_____ **4.** acts as the control center for your body

_____ **5.** includes your brain and spinal cord

_____ **6.** connects all areas of your body to the brain and spinal cord

THE PERIPHERAL NERVOUS SYSTEM

7. Nerve cells specialized to receive and conduct electrical impulses are

called _____.

8. Electrical messages, called _____, may travel as fast as
150 m/s or as slow as 0.2 m/s.

9. A large region in the neuron that contains a nucleus and cell organelles is

called the _____.

10. A neuron receives information from other cells through its

_____.

11. Impulses are carried away from the cell body by _____.

12. The tip of each branch of an axon is called a(n) _____.

13. Specialized nerve endings on sensory neurons that detect changes inside

and outside the body are called _____.

14. Neurons that send impulses from the brain and spinal cord to other systems

are called _____.

NERVES

_____ **15.** Nerves do NOT contain
    a. muscle fiber.
    b. blood vessels.
    c. axons.
    d. connective tissue.

16. Nerves may contain the axons of both _____ and

_____ neurons.

SOMATIC AND AUTONOMIC NERVOUS SYSTEMS

_____ **17.** The two main kinds of neurons in the peripheral nervous system are
    a. neurons and cell bodies.
    b. nerve cells and brain cells.
    c. CNS and PNS.
    d. sensory neurons and motor neurons.

18. The _____ of the peripheral nervous system are

somatic and autonomic neurons.

Mark each of the following statements *S* for somatic nervous system or *A* for autonomic nervous system.

_____ **19.** is under your conscious control

_____ **20.** controls digestion and heart rate

_____ **21.** is composed of the sympathetic and parasympathetic nervous systems

_____ **22.** is used for writing, talking, and other voluntary movements

_____ **23.** maintains a stable internal environment (homeostasis)

THE CENTRAL NERVOUS SYSTEM

24. What is the largest organ of the central nervous system?

_____

Mark each of the following actions *V* for voluntary or *I* for involuntary.

_____ **25.** digesting food

_____ **26.** moving your arm

27. The three connected parts of the brain are the _____, the

_____, and the _____.

28. Most memories are stored in the _____.

29. The right hand is controlled by the _____ hemisphere of

the cerebrum.

30. Which part of the brain keeps track of your body's position?

_____

31. Your body's involuntary processes, such as heart rate, are controlled

by the _____.

THE SPINAL CORD

32. The spinal cord is made of _____ and

_____.

33. The spinal cord is protected by _____.

34. Axons in your spinal cord allow your brain to communicate

with your _____ nervous system.

35. A spinal cord injury may block all information to and from

the _____.

36. What is a possible effect of a spinal cord injury?

_____

_____

37. What is one way to help prevent spinal cord injuries related to sports?

_____

_____

_____

Skills Worksheet

Directed Reading B

Section: Sensing the Environment (pp. 534–541)

1. How do you know when someone is tapping on your shoulder if you don't see him or her?

_____

_____

SENSE OF TOUCH

_____ 2. Skin is part of the
  a. digestive system.
  b. cardiovascular system.
  c. nervous system.
  d. integumentary system.

3. A thermoreceptor responds to changes in _____.

4. What does the integumentary system do for the body?

_____

_____

RESPONDING TO SENSORY MESSAGES

5. An involuntary and almost immediate response to a stimulus is

called a(n) _____.

6. A cycle of events in which one step controls or affects a previous

step is a(n) _____.

SENSE OF SIGHT

_____ 7. Why does a carrot look orange?
  a. The carrot absorbs orange light.
  b. The carrot deflects blue light to the eyes.
  c. The carrot reflects orange light to the eyes.
  d. The carrot refracts blue light to the eyes.

Match the correct description with the correct term. Write the letter in the space provided.

_____ **8.** is a photoreceptor needed to see color

_____ **9.** is an opening in the eye

_____ **10.** carries nerve impulses from photoreceptors

_____ **11.** protects the eye and allows light to enter

_____ **12.** is a neuron that changes light into electrical impulses

_____ **13.** is a photoreceptor important for night vision

_____ **14.** is the light-sensitive layer in the back of the eye

a. cornea

b. pupil

c. retina

d. optic nerve

e. rod

f. cone

g. photoreceptor

15. The part of the eye that gives it color and controls the light passing to the

retina is the _____.

16. How does the shape of the lens change in order to focus on an object?

_____

_____

17. Which type of vision problem occurs when the lens of the eye focuses light in front of the retina instead of on the retina?

_____

18. If you want to correct farsightedness, you should choose a lens that

is _____.

SENSE OF HEARING

19. When vibrations push on air particles, which push on other air particles,

they create _____ energy.

Put the following statements in the proper sequence from 1 to 5 to explain how we hear. Write the appropriate number in the space provided.

_____ **20.** One of the tiny ear bones vibrates against a fluid-filled organ.

_____ **21.** Inside the cochlea, vibrations create waves.

_____ **22.** Sound waves are funneled to the ear canal.

_____ **23.** Neurons convert waves into electrical impulses and send them to the brain.

_____ **24.** The eardrum vibrates against tiny bones.

25. A coiled tube found in the inner ear is the _____.

26. The _____ gathers sound waves and directs them to the ear canal.

27. Hair cells in the _____ respond to changes in the position of your head with respect to gravity.

SENSE OF TASTE

_____ **28.** Tiny bumps that cover the tongue are called
    a. taste cells.   **c.** taste buds.
    b. papillae.   **d.** olfactory cells.

_____ **29.** Which of the following contain clusters of taste receptors?
    a. taste cells.   **c.** taste buds.
    b. papillae.   **d.** olfactory cells.

_____ **30.** The receptors for taste are called
    a. taste cells.   **c.** taste buds.
    b. papillae.   **d.** olfactory cells.

31. Taste cells respond to saltiness, sweetness, sourness,

and _____.

SENSE OF SMELL

32. Smell receptors located in the upper part of your nasal cavity are

called _____.

33. The sensation of flavor happens when the brain combines information from

your taste buds and your _____.

Skills Worksheet

Vocabulary and Section Summary B

The Nervous System
VOCABULARY

After you finish reading the section, try this puzzle! Unscramble the letters at the end of each description to find the word that is being described.

1. system in your body responsible for gathering and interpreting information about the body's internal and external environment: URSVNEO

   _____

2. subdivision of question 1; includes your brain and spinal cord: ANRCELT

   _____

3. subdivision of question 1; includes everything except the brain and spinal cord: LIPPERHARE

   _____

4. specialized cells that transfer messages as electrical energy: NENORUS

   _____

5. axons that are bundled together with blood vessels and connective tissue: NSREVE

   _____

6. the largest organ of the central nervous system: ARNIB

   _____

SECTION SUMMARY

Read the following section summary.

The central nervous system (CNS) is the brain and the spinal cord.

The peripheral nervous system (PNS) is all of the parts of the nervous system except for the brain and spinal cord.

Nerves in the peripheral nervous system are bundles of axons, blood vessels, and connective tissue.

Sensory neurons have receptors that detect information about the body and its environment. Motor neurons carry messages from the brain and spinal cord to other parts of the body.

The PNS has two types of motor neurons: somatic neurons and autonomic neurons.

The cerebrum is the largest part of the brain and controls thinking, sensing, and voluntary movement.

The cerebellum is the part of the brain that keeps track of the body's position and that helps maintain balance.

The medulla controls involuntary processes, such as breathing and the regulation of heart rate, blood pressure, and body temperature.

Vocabulary and Section Summary B

Sensing the Environment
VOCABULARY

After you finish reading the section, try this puzzle! Use the clues given to fill in the blanks below. Then, copy the numbered letters into the appropriate boxes on the following page to reveal the answer to the bonus question.

1. an immediate, involuntary response to a stimulus

    __ __ __ __ __ __
     2

2. the opening through which light enters the eye

    __ __ __ __ __
      5 1

3. the organ system that includes hair, skin, and nails

    __ __ __ __ __ __ __ __ __ __ __ __ __
       10 3   12

4. the muscle that surrounds the pupil

    __ __ __ __
      7

5. when information from one step controls or affects a previous step

    __ __ __ __ __ __ __ __   __ __ __ __ __ __ __ __ __ __
         9   4

6. a coiled tube found in the inner ear that is essential for hearing

    __ __ __ __ __ __ __ __
     11   6

7. a layer of light-sensitive cells at the back of the eye

    __ __ __ __ __ __
       8

BONUS QUESTION

8. What are four sensations detected by receptors in the skin?

a.

___ ___ ___ ___ ___ ___ ___ ___
 1   2   3   4   4   5   2   3

b.

___ ___ ___ ___
 1   6   7   8

c.

V ___ ___ ___ ___ ___ ___ ___
    7   9   2   6 10   7 11   8

d.

___ ___ ___ ___ ___ ___ ___ ___ ___ ___ ___
10   3 12   1   3   2   6 10   5   2   3

SECTION SUMMARY

Read the following section summary.

Touch allows you to respond to temperature, pressure, pain, and vibration on the skin.

Reflexes and feedback mechanisms help you respond to your environment.

Sight allows you to respond to light energy. The eye has specialized structures to respond to light.

Hearing allows you to respond to sound energy. The ear has specialized structures to respond to the information in sound waves.

Taste allows you to distinguish flavors.

Smell allows you to perceive various odors.

Skills Worksheet)

Directed Reading B

Section: Human Reproduction (pp. 556–561)
THE MALE REPRODUCTIVE SYSTEM

Match the correct description with the correct term. Write the letter in the space provided.

_____ 1. place where male's sperm are produced

_____ 2. male hormone that regulates the development of sperm

_____ 3. mixture of sperm and other fluids

_____ 4. place where sperm mix with fluid

_____ 5. tube that stores sperm

_____ 6. tube through which semen is carried out of the penis

_____ 7. male's exterior sex organ

_____ 8. when a sperm enters an egg

a. testes

b. urethra

c. epididymis

d. semen

e. vas deferens

f. testosterone

g. penis

h. fertilization

THE FEMALE REPRODUCTIVE SYSTEM

_____ 9. A female's eggs and her sex hormones are produced in her
   a. zygote.
   b. estrogen.
   c. fallopian tubes.
   d. ovaries.

_____ 10. An egg travels into a fallopian tube during
   a. menstruation.
   b. ovulation.
   c. fertilization.
   d. pregnancy.

_____ 11. Fallopian tubes connect the ovaries with the
   a. uterus.
   b. zygote.
   c. vagina.
   d. eggs.

_____ **12.** A zygote develops in the female's
    a. ovary.
    b. vagina.
    c. uterus.
    d. placenta.

_____ **13.** The canal between the outside of the body and the uterus is the
    a. zygote.
    b. placenta.
    c. vagina.
    d. fallopian tubes.

14. When does a woman begin menstruating? When does menstruation usually end?

_____

_____

15. On the first day of the menstrual cycle, what does the uterus discharge?

_____

16. What occurs on about the 14th day of the menstrual cycle?

_____

17. About how long does a complete menstrual cycle last?

_____

ERTILIZATION

18. When must sperm be present in the female's reproductive system for fertilization to occur?

_____

MULTIPLE BIRTHS

19. Children who are born at the same time and who share the exact same

genes are called _____.

20. Of all twin births, identical twins make up about _____.

21. Children who are born at the same time but who can look very different

from each other are called _____.

22. A rare type of multiple birth occurring when a mother gives birth to five

babies is called _____.

Directed Reading B *continued*

REPRODUCTIVE SYSTEM PROBLEMS

_____ **23.** Which one of the following is a sexually transmitted disease (STD)?
  a. influenza
  b. tuberculosis
  c. herpes
  d. smallpox

_____ **24.** How can an infected person pass on an STD to another person?
  a. through sneezing
  b. through casual contact
  c. by shaking hands
  d. through sexual contact

_____ **25.** Hepatitis B is an STD that mainly affects which organ?
  a. the penis
  b. the heart
  c. the liver
  d. the uterus

_____ **26.** AIDS is an STD that is caused by
  a. herpes.   **c.** the immune system.
  b. a virus.   **d.** poor hygiene.

_____ **27.** Which one of the following is a common reproductive system cancer among men?
  a. cancer of the prostate
  b. cancer of the liver
  c. cancer of the vas deferens
  d. cancer of the blood

_____ **28.** Which one of the following is a common reproductive system cancer among women?
  a. cancer of the vagina
  b. cancer of the breast
  c. cancer of the neck
  d. cancer of the fallopian tubes

_____ **29.** What percentage of couples in the United States have difficulty producing offspring?
  a. 5   **c.** 15
  b. 10   **d.** 20

30. How often do STDs cause infertility in men as compared to women?

_____

_____

Skills Worksheet

Directed Reading B

Section: Growth and Development (pp. 562–567)

FROM FERTILIZATION TO EMBRYO

_____ 1. Ordinarily, how many sperm fertilize a female's egg?
   a. several million
   b. a few hundred
   c. one
   d. six to ten

_____ 2. An egg is fertilized after the union of the egg's and sperm's
   a. membranes.
   b. nuclei.
   c. semen.
   d. zygote.

_____ 3. About 5 days after fertilization, the egg arrives at the
   a. fallopian tubes.
   b. vagina.
   c. cervix.
   d. uterus.

_____ 4. Which one of the following is a characteristic of an embryo?
   a. It is a tiny ball of cells.
   b. It is not yet fertilized.
   c. It develops in the vagina.
   d. It is less than 1 day old.

FROM EMBRYO TO FETUS

_____ 5. Which of the following is a characteristic of the placenta?
   a. It's an exchange organ between mother and embryo.
   b. It contains very few blood vessels.
   c. It becomes an organ in the developing embryo.
   d. It contracts to help the mother give birth.

_____ 6. The child developing inside the mother's uterus is connected to the placenta by a tube called
   a. the vagina.
   b. an embryo.
   c. the amnion.
   d. the umbilical cord.

_____ **7.** After 10 weeks, a developing embryo is called a(n)
   a. amnion.
   b. fetus.
   c. zygote.
   d. placenta.

Match the correct description with the correct term. Write the letter in the space provided.

_____ **8.** The embryo's blood cells begin to form.

_____ **9.** The spinal cord and regions of the brain begin to develop.

_____ **10.** The fetus's eyes can respond to light.

_____ **11.** The fetus doubles in size and begins to move.

_____ **12.** The fetus is able to hear sounds.

a. weeks 2–4
b. weeks 5–8
c. weeks 9–16
d. weeks 17–24
e. weeks 25–36

BIRTH

_____ **13.** The mother's muscle contractions that help a baby to be born are called
   a. the uterus.
   b. the placenta.
   c. labor.
   d. full term.

_____ **14.** Your navel is the place on your body that was once attached to
   a. the uterus.
   b. the amnion.
   c. a fallopian tube.
   d. the umbilical cord.

FROM BIRTH TO DEATH

_____ **15.** Which of the following is a characteristic of infancy?
   a. Baby teeth appear.
   b. You begin to run.
   c. You begin to read.
   d. You need little sleep.

_____ **16.** Which of the following is a characteristic of childhood?
   a. You grow relatively slowly.
   b. You lose flexibility.
   c. You produce sex hormones.
   d. You grow permanent teeth.

17. You become an adolescent after you have reached _____.

18. What are two ways in which a male's body changes after puberty?

_____

19. What are two ways in which a female's body changes after puberty?

_____

20. What are two early signs of aging in adults under the age of 40?

_____

21. What are two signs of aging in adults over the age of 65?

_____

Skills Worksheet

Vocabulary and Section Summary B

Human Reproduction
VOCABULARY

After you finish reading the section, try this puzzle! The underlined words below are scrambled. Write the completed words in the spaces provided.

1. The <u>SIPEN</u> transfers sperm from the male to the female.

_____

2. The <u>YVOAR</u> produces eggs in the female.

_____

3. Sperm are produced by the <u>STETSE</u>.

_____

4. The <u>GAVANI</u> connects the outside of the body to the uterus.

_____

5. A human embryo develops into a fetus in the <u>TURESU</u>.

_____

SECTION SUMMARY

Read the following section summary.

The male reproductive system produces sperm and can deliver sperm to the female reproductive system.

The female reproductive system produces eggs, nurtures zygotes, and gives birth.

If sperm are present in the female reproductive system within a few days of ovulation, fertilization may occur.

A fertilized egg has one chromosome from each chromosome pair of the parents.

Humans usually have one child per birth, but some people have multiple births.

Human reproduction can be affected by infertility and by diseases such as cancer.

Skills Worksheet

Vocabulary and Section Summary B

Growth and Development

VOCABULARY

After you finish reading the section, try this puzzle! Use the clues below to find the correct term. Then, find those words in the puzzle on the following page. Terms can be hidden in the puzzle vertically, horizontally, or backward.

_____ 1. This is a partly fetal and partly maternal organ that exchanges materials between the mother and fetus.

_____ 2. This begins on the first day of a woman's last menstrual period.

_____ 3. This is a developing individual, from fertilization until the 10th week.

_____ 4. This is a developing individual from the end of the 10th week until birth.

_____ 5. This connects the fetus to the placenta.

S	Y	G	Q	E	V	Y	T	Z	A	H	Z	Y	S
F	D	P	L	V	A	D	K	S	T	Q	F	E	E
A	T	H	E	Z	J	K	J	E	Y	Z	E	H	A
J	H	A	T	Q	P	L	A	C	E	N	T	A	H
Z	Q	H	Y	Z	C	Z	Y	D	J	E	U	F	Y
Q	J	E	E	E	H	S	Q	X	Q	F	S	D	T
U	M	B	I	L	I	C	A	L	C	O	R	D	X
Y	V	A	C	A	H	T	H	D	J	Y	T	J	D
S	Y	E	Q	K	D	Z	T	E	H	R	D	Q	Y
G	D	X	S	J	A	V	S	V	Z	B	T	J	S
E	Q	T	K	Q	K	E	A	Y	Q	M	H	Q	H
A	D	H	E	J	D	T	H	G	V	E	V	A	T
Y	C	N	A	N	G	E	R	P	T	Y	J	S	Y
Q	D	C	S	F	Z	A	X	E	D	Z	Q	T	A

SECTION SUMMARY

Read the following section summary.

Fertilization occurs when a sperm from the male joins with an egg from the female.

First as an embryo and then as a fetus, a developing human undergoes many changes between implantation and birth.

During the development of a human, cells differentiate.

The umbilical cord and placenta support the developing human during pregnancy by providing oxygen and nutrients and by removing waste materials.

The first stage of human development lasts from fertilization to birth.

After birth, a human goes through four more stages of growth and development.